product

in association with the Bunker Theatre present

# KILLYMUCK

by Kat Woods

This production is kindly supported by

Supported using public funding by
**ARTS COUNCIL
ENGLAND**
LOTTERY FUNDED

THE
CARNE TRUST
*Supporting young talent in the performing arts*

The people of Tavistock worshipped in the early thirteenth century parish church of St Eustachius, only yards from the great abbey church. Their daily lives must have been regulated by the Offices of the abbey. The main entrance to the abbey enclave was at Court Gate and there was much routine contact between the abbot's men and the laity. The abbey maintained an infirmary and also ran the Hospital of St Mary Magdalene for lepers, on the western edge of the town; no doubt the townspeople received specialist help when necessary. The abbey also served as a centre for learning. A small school was run to train boys for the priesthood, but an education was also offered to the sons of the laity of Tavistock, even if the boys went on to secular careers. The Master of the School in the 1530s was John Elyott, who taught his half dozen or so pupils the Benedictine Rule, Latin and theology. Literacy was reckoned valuable by those wealthy merchants who could afford to send their sons to school, rather than setting them to work early.[34]

The abbey could also lay claim to a major technological advance in the West Country. The fifteenth-century invention of the printing press had been brought to England by William Caxton in the 1470s, but by the 1520s there were only half a dozen centres in England where printing was carried out, all in the eastern counties. The first printing press in the South West was set up by Thomas Richard in Tavistock in 1525, and the first book printed by the monks was Boethius' work *The Consolation of Philosophy*. This pioneering work was in many ways typical of the abbey of Tavistock, which had also introduced agricultural improvements on the Manor of Hurdwick and set new standards in architecture in the town.[27]

The essential basis for the abbot's power in the town, however, lay in his role as landlord. There were perhaps a couple of thousand men, women and children living in Tavistock and on the surrounding Manor of Hurdwick, and the great majority lived on holdings or in tenements leased from the abbey. Even more substantial freeholders usually also rented lands from the abbey. The burgage rents in the borough of Tavistock, an administrative district of 325 acres, were fixed at an average of 8d. per annum, while most of the holdings in the rural hinterland were leased either for the lifetime of the lessee and two others, usually his wife and his son, or for forty years. Among the many tenants and freeholders there were several leading families, notably the Hawkins and Amadas families, and one Richard Drake. There was also the Fitz family, the Poynters, the Maynards, the Glanvilles and several other well-established Tavistock families, including the Drakes of Crowndale. Most of the tenements and gardens were on the north side of the river, along West Street, Ford Street and Bannawell Street, and the impression is of houses each with their own plot of land, in the medieval fashion, rather than a dense concentration of buildings. There were dovecotes, pigsties and meadows within the town, and tenants were expected to maintain their hedges, ditches and gates. On the south side of the river was the abbot's deer park: beyond that the land rose steeply into the wastes of the moor.[1,7]

For half a millenium this had been the established order at Tavistock. The daily round of Offices said in the abbey, the concern of the abbot for the

*Court Gate looking from the site of the Great Court of the Abbey*

*West Street, looking east towards Dartmoor*

spiritual and economic welfare of the townspeople, provided a familiar framework for the grandparents and parents of Francis Drake. But a couple of years before he was born, all this was swept away and a new order imposed on the ancient town. Tavistock at the time of Drake's birth was the scene of revolutionary changes.

*Part of the cloisters of Tavistock Abbey*

# 2

# The New Order

The 1530s were a time of great change in England. The King, Henry VIII, denied papal permission to divorce his first wife Catherine of Aragon in order to marry Ann Boleyn in the hope of getting a son, made himself head of the English Church instead of the Pope. Under the new dispensation, Henry granted himself a divorce. But the monasteries clung to the old order, owing a special duty to Rome; moreover the monasteries owned vast estates. Jealous of his new position, as Supreme Head of the Church in England, and always in need of more money, Henry cast covetous eyes on the monastic properties of England. In 1536 the smaller houses were dissolved; in 1539 the great abbeys were surrendered; and by 1540 a centuries-old tradition had ended.[39]

In Tavistock the end came on 3rd March 1539, when the royal commissioner accepted the abbot's deed of surrender. At Glastonbury an example had been made of the abbot, who was hanged before his gates for treason, but at Tavistock, the abbot, John Peryn and his twenty monks, quietly accepted their fate. There were pensions for them, and John Peryn lived on comfortably in West Street for another ten years. Meanwhile the abbey was stripped of all its valuables to raise money for the king. The gold and silver ornaments from the shrine of St Rumon were taken to London, the great bells weighing half a ton were taken down and sold, and the lead was stripped from the roof. By the time the commissioners had finished with Tavistock Abbey there was little left for others to pick over.

The abbey estates were another matter. Generally, Henry sold the lands he had acquired, creating a large new class of gentleman landowners who profited from the dissolution of the monasteries. Buckland Abbey, a few miles south of Tavistock, went the way of most estates and was sold to the Grenville family. But Tavistock Abbey lands were not sold: they were granted to Lord John Russell, the President of the newly created Council of the West.

# THE WEST VIEW OF TAVISTOCK-ABBY, IN THE COUNTY OF DEVON.

To the most Noble JOHN,

Duke and Earl of Bedford, Marquefs of Tavistock, Baron Rufsel of Thornhaugh, and Baron Howland of Streatham: Proprietor of these Remains

This Profpect is humbly Infcrib'd by Your Graces most Dutiful, and Obedient Servants. Anon.° & Nath.° Buck.

*Original was or is in the Dukes of Devonshire & Cornwall, whose Daughters was marryed to St. Edgars. Ordgarus or Ordgar, who probably founded it out here, till his son Oddulph built the abbey about 961, for then the whole Manner of Tavistock & their adorations therefore, was given to the Monastery about 1140: of Frank Pledge, Gallows, Pillory &c: & of great Extent: The Church was dedicated to St. Mary & St. Rumon. The Danes burnt the abbey soon rebuilt. In the Reign of K. Ed.² the abbot claim'd the aforesaid Privileges which were by that King allow'd & confirm'd. There were divers famous Men & Abbots the most particular of two Bishops Kone etc. of Devonshire: of the Courtenay family, Lieut. in very fav.us in the Saxon Language to preserve in Memory; divers of the Dignity of the Mitred Abbots who sat as Barons, in Parliament: Their Power and Privileges continued till the Diffolution by K of K. who gave it to Robin L.º Rufsel etc. which Noble Family is still continued. January Value £902-5-7¼. Isº R. Buck. delin et sculp 1734.*

Reproduced by A. Wheaton & Co. Ltd. for Devon Books, 1984.

*The west view of Tavistock Abbey*

Under Henry VIII, three councils were set up to govern areas remote from the central administration in London. The Councils of the North and Wales dealt with the marcher territories of the borders, while the Council of the West was set to enforce the king's writ in the equally remote South West, where men were conservative and reluctant to accept Henry's new policies. The Council of the West was responsible for the administration of Dorset, Somerset, Devon and Cornwall and its quarterly sessions met at Dorchester, Wells, Exeter and Tavistock. For part of the year, then, Tavistock was the seat of the provincial government. As the representative of the King, the President of the Council of the West required sufficient estates to support his new vice, regal dignity. Lord Russell had some lands in Dorset but these were deemed insufficient and he was granted property at Blackawton and Exeter, most of the Dunkeswell Abbey estates, and the greater part of Tavistock Abbey, its site and its lands. The Council of the West met for five years, until 1543, when the changes produced by the dissolution of the monasteries had worked their way through and were accepted. But Lord Russell remained the chief representative of the government in the South West, and in Tavistock all the secular powers previously held by the abbey now belonged to him.[27]

The people of Tavistock, governed so closely as they had been by the abbey, experienced the full impact of the Reformation at first hand. In much of the rest of England there was little general understanding of the profound changes Henry had set in train. The Pope was now merely the Bishop of Rome, with no powers over the English Church, and the King was now the administrative head of the Church but there was no official change in doctrine. Mass was still said in the familiar fashion, and many of the dispossessed monks simply became members of the clergy. Freed from the control of Rome, the new Church of England was open to reform in wider spheres, and reformers came flocking from the Continent, eager to replace the old corrupt structure with a new Protestant Church. Henry, however, maintained the Catholic forms: although towns like Tavistock experienced great changes, these were economic and social rather than religious changes.[38]

The services that the abbey had provided for the town ceased with its dissolution. The school was closed, the hospitality that the abbey had traditionally offered to travellers ended, the infirmary closed, the relief given to the poor of the town discontinued and the great annual fair of St Rumon was no longer held. No more books were printed in the South West for one hundred and fifty years. The terms of the many leaseholds now owned by Lord Russell were also changed. Most of the rents were not increased, but in every case, instead of the existing three-life leases, these were shortened to two lives, that of the tenant and his wife. As a result, within a few years many of these leases would be due for renewal and Lord Russell would be able to collect fresh entry fines from each new tenant. The dissolution of Tavistock Abbey had thus changed the pattern of life in Tavistock and it was into this new, disturbed era, that Francis Drake was born.[1,27]

*Drake's birthplace, Crowndale, looking from East Crowndale across the River Tavy to Crowndale Farm*

# 3

# The Drakes of Tavistock

**B**y the sixteenth century the Drake family was well established in Tavistock and the surrounding area. At Newton, Henry Drake, who leased a tenement and corn mill there, was followed by Elize Drake; in Tavistock itself one Thomas Drake followed another as the lessee of a cottage and garden; and another Drake, William, whose occupation was noted as smith, also rented property in Tavistock at the same time. A wealthier branch of the family was represented by Richard Drake, who was rated as one of the richest men in town in the 1523 subsidy rolls; in the later years of the century his son, also Richard Drake, succeeded him as one of the leading men of Tavistock. At Whitchurch, a mile or so south of Tavistock, the vicar of St Andrews church from 1524 to 1547 was William Drake; and there was another substantial branch of the family at Crowndale, a hamlet in the valley of the Tavy a mile downstream from the town. The exact relationship between these various families of Drakes is uncertain but probably they were all descended from one family, perhaps as far back as the thirteenth century. It is likely that, in the way of the Tudors, they counted each other as kin.[1]

The Drakes of Crowndale had first settled there in 1441, when Henry Drake leased land from the abbot for the customary forty years. Before the Black Death in the middle of the fourteenth century, Crowndale had been a thriving hamlet, part of the original demesne lands of the abbey, supporting seven holdings and a corn mill on the lower reaches of the Tavy. After the plague, these holdings had been reduced to one. During the fifteenth century the valley slowly came to life again. The corn mill was rebuilt as a fulling mill and known subsequently as Shillamill, and lands were leased at this lower end of the valley to the Coche family. Their neighbours, nearer to Tavistock, were the Drakes of Crowndale, where Henry Drake was followed by Simon Drake in 1481, and Simon in his turn was succeeded by John and Margery Drake.

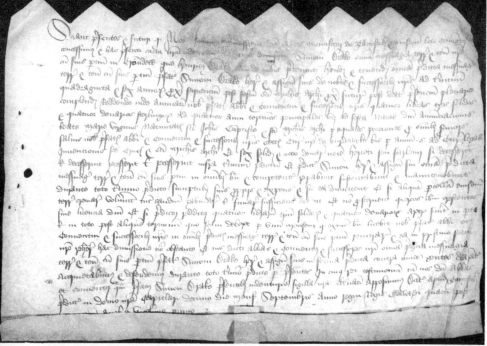

*The lease of Crowndale Farm to Simon Drake 1481*

*The lease of Crowndale Farm to John Drake 1520*

There was a second Drake property in Crowndale, where lands were held from the abbey by a further branch of the family, John and Edmund Drake.[1]

Francis Drake was probably born in 1541 or 1542. The exact site of Drake's birthplace is not known. That it was in Crowndale and not in Kent, where the family moved in 1549, is clear both from the evidence produced by a young relative, John Drake, captured by the Inquisition and interrograted about his family background, and from the statements made by a contemporary historian, Camden.[20] Both Camden and John Drake state that Francis Drake was born in Crowndale near Tavistock. The valley known as Crowndale is divided by the River Tavy and the farm to the west, in Tavistock parish, was leased by John and Margery Drake, the grandparents of Francis Drake. On the eastern side of the Tavy, in Whitchurch parish, were two farms known as East and West Crowndale. The farm of West Crowndale was also leased to a family of Drakes; an Edmund Drake was succeeded by the 1540s by another John Drake. Simultaneously then, there were two branches of the Drake family farming in Crowndale, each family bearing the same Christian names. There was John Drake the elder on the west side of the river, with his sons John Drake junior and Edmund Drake, while on the east side of the Tavy farmed Edmund Drake and his son John. The relationship between two families is not known but it seems likely that they were closely related. Possibly John Drake the elder of Crowndale was brother to Edmund Drake of West Crowndale.

The two families of Drakes were comparatively wealthy. In the Lay Subsidy Rolls of 1543 and 1545, giving the taxation returns, John Drake of West Crowndale was rated at £8, well above the average for Whitchurch parish, and one Joan Drake, widow, possibly his mother, at £4. In Tavistock parish John Drake of Crowndale paid £20, John Drake junior £5 and Edmund Drake £4: the average for Tavistock parish was £3.[1] Edmund, a shearman by trade, married in about 1540 and had a large family: his eldest son was Francis Drake.[12] With their comfortable background, it seems likely that Edmund Drake and his wife had their own cottage in Crowndale, most probably built of the local stone from a nearby quarry; or they may have continued to live with his parents in the farmhouse. Any such cottage must have been built above the flood plain of the Tavy and there are foundations of old houses on both sides of the river. Most probably the Edmund Drakes would have lived on his parents' farm, on the west side of the Tavy; but they may have lived on John Drake's land, on the Whitchurch side. The two farms were connected by a footpath crossing the Tavy by means of a ford and quite likely some of the agricultural work was carried on communally.

There are traditions which support both possibilities. It has long been held that Drake was born on the larger holding which continued to support a large farmhouse. Estate office surveys of two hundred years after the event put his birthplace on the Tavistock parish side.[20] However, there is also a long tradition in Whitchurch that Drake's birthplace fell within their parish. There is no conclusive proof; Drake remains simply Francis Drake of Crowndale.

There is also a tradition that Francis Russell, the son and heir of Lord John

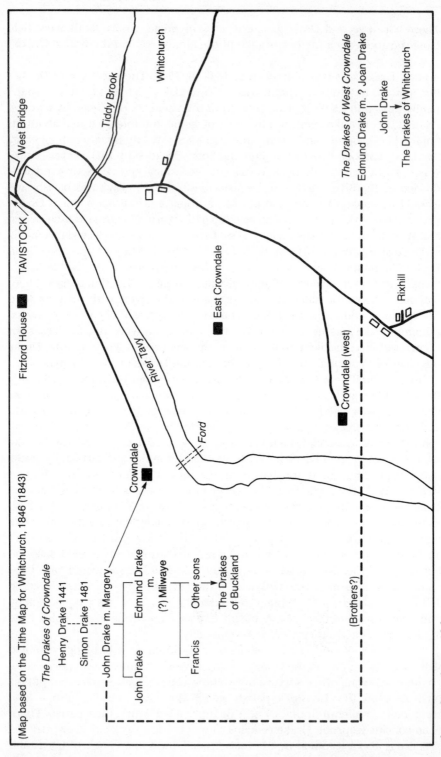

(Map based on the Tithe Map for Whitchurch, 1846 (1843))

*The Drakes of Crowndale*

Henry Drake 1441

Simon Drake 1481

*The Drakes of West Crowndale*

Edmund Drake m. ? Joan Drake

John Drake

The Drakes of Whitchurch

West Bridge

Fitzford House ■   TAVISTOCK

Whitchurch

*Tiddy Brook*

□

□

East Crowndale ■

River Tavy

Rixhill

□ □
□

Crowndale (west) ■

*Ford*

Crowndale ■

John Drake m. Margery

John Drake

Edmund Drake
m.
(?) Milwaye

Francis

Other sons

The Drakes of Buckland

(Brothers?)

*The Drakes of Crowndale*

Russell, was godfather to the baby Francis at his christening and that the baby was named after him. This is supported by the fact that Francis was not a traditional Drake family name: William, Thomas or John were the usual choices. Francis' early childhood was spent in the valley of Crowndale, perhaps on his grandparents' farm, where he would have been expected to make himself useful doing simple agricultural tasks. There were probably cousins to play with, the weekly trip into town for the Friday market, and the regular attendance at church; and as Francis grew older and more adventurous there was the River Tavy to ford, Morwelldown to climb, and a host of friends and relatives to visit.

In the closely-knit community of Tavistock, the Drakes were connected to many other families. The Maynards were cousins to the Reverend William Drake of Whitchurch,[9] who may well have been Francis' great uncle. Later, Drakes married into the Glanville family; and Francis' mother was probably a Hawkins.[8] The relationship with the Hawkins family was, in the event, extremely important in Drake's future career. One of the Tavistock Hawkins, William, moved down to Plymouth in about 1515 to ship out the family tin and wool.[30] This William Hawkins founded the dynasty of merchant adventurers in Plymouth, but he retained leased land in Tavistock and buttressed the family fortunes by a marriage alliance with the Amadas family, who were the owners of most of the mills in Tavistock.[1] There was also a close friendship between the Drakes and the Fitz family of Tavistock, who were gentlemen and entitled to carry arms. Notwithstanding the social differences, in 1483 Walter Fitz had appointed William Drake to be his executor. Through this friendship with the Fitz family the Drakes were known to the Tremaynes, and indeed the Reverend William Drake had been presented with his first living, at Sydenham, by the Tremaynes. Thus the Drakes were woven firmly into the fabric of life at Tavistock, and this network of friends and relatives stood the young Francis Drake in good stead all his life.[20]

*An early nineteenth-century engraving of the supposed sited of Drake's birthplace*

*The Abbot's House, now known as Betsy Grimbal's Tower*

# 4
# Drake's Tavistock

---

The Tavistock that Drake knew as a boy was still dominated by the empty shell of the abbey. Between the parish church of St Eustachius and the river lay the great abbey church, the cloisters and other monastic offices. But with the lead stripped from the roofs, and no one left to care for them, the abbey buildings were increasingly dilapidated. The river bounded the abbey site on the east, while to the south the abbot's lodging still stood, enjoying the pleasant prospect of the abbey meadows stretching down to Fitzford House and West Bridge. The Court Gate, opening into the decaying precincts of the Great Court of the abbey, had been the main thoroughfare between the abbey and town, but in Drake's day the hub of activity lay outside the abbey gates.

The centre of Tavistock was a network of narrow lanes that had grown up, haphazardly, in the shelter of the abbey. Shops opened directly on to the streets, usually with a workshop at the back and a narrow strip of garden behind that butted on to other tenements. The trades that were carried on within the borough were many and varied. There were shoemakers, glaziers, tilers, masons, cordwainers, glovers, weavers, cutlers, millers, barbers, clerks, plumbers and labourers, all working side by side along St Matthew Street, Bedford Street, Lower Market Street and the other lanes opening off these.[7] Most of the craftsmen also kept livestock – hens, a pig or two, perhaps a cow or some sheep pastured on the edge of town. On market day, when the smallholders and labourers came into town with produce carried in panniers on the backs of ponies or donkeys, the unpaved streets outside Court Gate would be crowded with stalls and customers. Probably the lanes were churned into mud by the end of the day, with pigs rooting through the rubbish left behind by the stallholders.

Several open conduits flowed through the streets of Tavistock, bringing

*The River Tavy in Tavistock looking upstream to Abbey Bridge*

water for the town households and carrying away sewage. One stream, the Fishlake, flowed down Bannawell Street to Market Street and round the parish church to join the Tavy near Court Gate. From Parkwood on the eastern edge of the borough, water was drawn from the Tavy and carried in a leat called the Millbrook along Brook Street, to power the town corn mill outside Court Gate before emptying itself into the Tavy again.[27] After heavy rain these channels probably scoured the streets clean of rubbish. Such sanitary arrangements, where polluted water was also used for drinking, commonly led to diseases such as cholera; but in Tavistock, where the hills were steep and the water ran swiftly, there may have been fewer outbreaks of disease. The River Tavy, one of the fastest flowing rivers in England, swept the town's rubbish away, provided sea trout and salmon for the townspeople, and powered corn mills and fulling mills.

The various water courses in Tavistock were crossed by several bridges in Drake's time. Within the town itself the conduits were crossed by numbers of footbridges serving the residents. Upstream of the abbey the Tavy was divided into two channels by a group of islands, and at the upper end of these islands was the Great Bridge of Tavistock, later known as the East Bridge. A narrow five-arched stone bridge, it was built in the thirteenth century and carried traffic from Plymouth, Whitchurch and Dartmoor into the town. Downstream of the Great Bridge there was a small private bridge from the Abbey Water Gate across to the Whitchurch road, probably falling into disrepair after the dissolution of the abbey. The Tavy was also crossed by a bridge, new when Drake was a boy, West Bridge, downstream from the abbey meadows. This replaced a ford that had served between Ford Street and the lanes leading up to Whitchurch and Walreddon. West Bridge was built using some stone from the abbey,[35] which was to serve as a convenient quarry for the people of Tavistock: many of the houses built in Tavistock during the next couple of centuries contain some stone from the abbey ruins.

Outside Court Gate there was the town corn mill driven by the Millbrook, and a fulling mill owned by the Amadas family, where newly woven cloth was shrunk and felted.[1] The material was beaten flat by hammers driven by the same stream. Cloth woven locally contained flock to soften the coarse fibres of Dartmoor fleeces, and was known in the trade as 'Tavistocks'. There were several fulling mills along the valley and Tavistock must have echoed to the noise of the fulling mill hammers.[27] The finished cloth was carried down to Morwell port, on the Tamar, or overland to Plymouth, by long trains of packhorses that must have caused further congestion in Tavistock's crowded streets. Much cloth was exported from the South West to Brittany, and the several Bretons living in Tavistock in the 1540s may have dealt in 'Tavistocks'.

The other main local industry was tin mining, and although the bulk of the tin was mined up on Dartmoor, there were mines at Parkwood on the eastern edge of the town and at Anderton in Whitchurch. Tin was much in demand as wooden bowls and platters were being replaced by pewter in the sixteenth century. There were pewterers in Tavistock, but most of the tin was bought by other factors, and more trains of packhorses wound through the narrow

*Looking through Court Gate to the nineteenth-century Guildhall*

lanes carrying the tin away for export. While wool and tin were the two main industries of the town, farming was naturally the mainstay for most people, and the packhorses probably brought lime by the bushel on the return journey, to fertilize the fields.

All leading merchants in Tavistock belonged to the Jesus Guild, which owned lands and tenements in the town.[7] Just before the dissolution of the abbey, the merchants built a Guildhall in the crowded centre of the town outside the abbey gates: to the young Francis, the Guildhall would have appeared raw and new. Probably the borough court, presided over by an official variously described as the portreeve or mayor, met in the Guildhall to deal with minor criminals. The pillory, for male offenders, probably stood at the foot of Kilworthy Hill and the skelving stool, for ducking women, may have been at the Fishlake or the Millbrook.

The population of Tavistock can be estimated from the Lay Subsidy Rolls of 1543, when Henry VIII ordered that everyone with land or goods worth £1 a year should be taxed. He needed money to pay for his war against the Scots; most other subsidies taxed only the wealthier men. In 1543 about two hundred and seventy people, mostly men but including some spinsters and widows, were liable to pay tax in Tavistock parish. These men, their families and servants, together with some poor families who did not pay the subsidy, made up the community of Tavistock. The chief men of the town, such as John Fitz and John Amadas, paid as much as £40: John Coche and his neighbour John Drake of Crowndale paid £20 each; and Edmund Drake, probably Francis' father, paid £4; while the average was £3.[1] The wealthiest men, especially those setting themselves up as gentlemen, did not live in the press of the town centre, with all its noise, smells and traffic. John Fitz and his family lived at Fitzford House, on the western edge of town. There were also some fine houses in West Street and the last abbot, John Peryn, is believed to have retired to a house at the top of West Street, with his feather beds and silverware.[27]

In some ways Tavistock, when Drake was a boy, was going through a period of transition from the ordered society dominated by the abbey into an uncertain future. The school had closed, the great excitements of the fair had ended and the poor could no longer obtain relief, although St Mary Magdalene, the lazar hospital on the western edge of the town, continued under Robert Isaac, relying on their income from leases.[7] The churchwardens of St Eustachius began in an ad hoc way to take on some of the other duties left to them. It was clear that for some years to come Lord John Russell was likely to be more preoccupied with affairs of state than with the small doings of his new property, Tavistock.

The last Abbot retired to a house at the top of West Street, near here

# 5

# The Apprentice

The childhood years of Francis Drake followed the natural rhythm of the seasons; ploughing, sowing, sheep shearing and harvest were succeeded by the annual autumn slaughter of beasts surplus to breeding requirements. There was also the church year, with its calendar of saints' days and festivals. In Tavistock there was the occasional excitement of coinage, when the tin dealers and pewter factors came to town to buy the tin assayed and stamped by the stannary officials. Some tin dealers came from as far afield as Italy or the Low Countries, bringing an unlikely cosmopolitan air to the little Devon Town for a few days.[31] News of the outside world came from a variety of sources - the Bishop of Exeter on his visitation, the merchants and their shipping associates, and the Russells with their contacts at court, where the old king was now married to his sixth and last wife, Catherine Parr. Henry VIII died in 1547, after nearly forty years on the throne, and was succeeded by his young son Edward, a boy of nine dominated by his uncle, the Duke of Somerset. Most men could not remember a time before Henry was king. In the next year or so, men were further unsettled by rumours of the changes the Protestant Duke of Somerset proposed for the Church.

In 1548 an incident occurred which shook the respectable Drake family. Edmund Drake, Francis' father, was indicted for robbing a man of his purse and then of horse stealing. He was pardoned for these crimes[27] but afterwards his position in Tavistock must have been uneasy. The events of 1549, however, when the West Country rose against enforced religious change, gave Edmund and his family the chance of a fresh start.

Under Henry VIII the Roman Catholic Church in England had become the Church of England; under Edward VI the Church of England became Protestant. A new Prayer Book was introduced on Whitsunday 1549, and its

*Market Street, the medieval trading centre of the town*

use enforced in every parish in England. This brought home the changes in doctrine to the ordinary people and in Devon and Cornwall, as conservative in religion as they were in most matters, there was rebellion. An army of Devon and Cornish farmers and labourers marched on Exeter to demand the reinstatement of the old Mass and the restoration of the abbeys. Lord John Russell, now the owner of the Tavistock abbey estates and one of the Protestant reformers himself, led the army that crushed the rising. In the meantime Edmund Drake, later known as a staunch Protestant, took his young family down to Plymouth in order, he said, to escape persecution. In the aftermath of the Prayer Book Rebellion the Edmund Drakes left Devon altogether and moved to Kent, probably shipped along the coast by the naval captain Richard Drake, or by their cousins the Hawkins. For the young Francis, now about seven or eight, a new life was beginning.

Edmund Drake and his family settled near the royal dockyards at Chatham on the River Medway in Kent. Home was an old ship, no longer in commission, and here the Drakes raised their twelve sons. At first they were poor indeed. For the boys' mother, far from home and family, the old hulk in Gillingham Reach was probably a poor exchange for the settled agricultural way of life in Devon. But for Edmund Drake there were new opportunities. He became a preacher to the fleet and, freed from the conservative Catholicism of Tavistock, was able to follow his Protestant inclination. He became a fervent evangelist. Under the Catholic Queen Mary I (1553-8), he remained a reader of prayers to the navy but once Elizabeth was queen, Protestantism was encouraged once more. In this new climate Edmund Drake was ordained deacon and soon became vicar of Upchurch in Kent.

The move to Kent also meant new opportunities for the Drake sons. Instead of farmers, at least three became sailors. A seaman's way of life came naturally to children who lived on a tidal reach surrounded by the navy. Formal education came from their Protestant father. Edmund Drake taught his sons to read, probably using the English Great Bible, and exhorted them to make the most of the Bible. Despite this new way of life, the family's Devon background was never forgotten. Francis Drake spoke with a Devon accent throughout his life, often spelling his name 'Frauncis'.[17] Since the Drakes were literate, links with relatives in Tavistock and Plymouth may have been maintained, though with difficulty.

Religious divisions between Catholic and Protestant continued to trouble the Drake family in Kent. While Francis Drake was still a boy, the Protestant reign of Edward VI ended and his sister Mary became queen. Half Spanish, wholly Catholic, Mary proposed to marry the Catholic King Philip of Spain, a marriage which she hoped would secure the Catholic succession in England. But her English subjects had become accustomed to services in English, married clergy, plainer churches and all the greater freedom which went with Protestantism, and were not inclined to follow their queen. In 1554 Thomas Wyatt of Kent led a rebellion against Mary; for the Drakes, the fighting came uncomfortably close when the royal fleet at Gillingham was attacked, while one of Wyatt's fellow conspirators, Nicholas Throckmorton, was later known to them as Member of Parliament for Tavistock.[11] The young Edmund Tremayne, certainly known from Tavistock days, was racked for his suspected part in the conspiracy.[10] The rebels failed: Wyatt was executed and in the aftermath Mary married Philip and imposed a rigid Catholicism that provoked some men into martyrdom and the majority into a bitter dislike of Catholics and Spain.[39] For the young Drake, Mary's reign was an object lesson which served to hammer home his father's teachings.

Francis Drake was apprenticed at an early age, perhaps ten or twelve, to the owner of a small coastal barque. These early years, spent manoevring in and out of east coast ports, with the occasional trip to Zeeland and France, taught Francis his trade as a seaman. Probably the boat was of shallow draught and broad-beamed, easily worked by a man and a boy. Here, in the Thames approaches and the east coast currents, he learned to pilot his craft. His diligence and skill so impressed his master that when the old man died he bequeathed his barque to his apprentice. This was the foundation of Drake's fortunes. He was one of twelve sons and could expect to inherit little from his parents, but he was now a master mariner in his own right. For several more years Drake continued to ply the east coast, trading in goods such as cloth, corn and herring, but this creeping from port to muddy port soon palled once he had mastered the skills. In about 1564, now in his early twenties, he sold the barque and moved back to Devon, where he enlisted into the trading fleet of the Hawkins family of Plymouth.[18]

From the ports of the West Country, ships were now sailing for the New World, where there was reputed to be fabulous wealth - diamonds, emeralds, gold and silver - to reward the first European traders. Under the new queen, Mary's Protestant half-sister Elizabeth, there was a fresh impetus in English adventuring across the Atlantic and the West Country families of ship-owners and traders were in the vanguard. The challenge of deep sea sailing, the sheer excitement and the riches that such adventurers could gain, must have attracted Drake. Given his character - courageous, daring and ambitious - it seems inevitable that he should have gravitated to the most exciting and demanding life available to a seaman.[15]

# 6
# *Early Expeditions*

D rake came to Plymouth with two great advantages, his natural abilities and his relationship with the Hawkins family. By the 1560s Plymouth had become the focus of English maritime enterprise directed towards the New World, and the Hawkins family were the most important in this field. Coming originally from Tavistock, the family's fortunes were based on a strong merchant fleet, supported by influential friends at court. Old William Hawkins had made three voyages to Brazil in the 1530s, trading in African ivory with the American Indians, and his sons William and John continued the family tradition of merchant adventuring.[40] As a young cousin of John Hawkins, later Treasurer of the Navy, Drake was taken on as a junior officer and sailed first to Spain in a merchantman. On his next voyage in 1566 he was promoted to second in command under Captain John Lovell who introduced Drake to the Atlantic slave trade. The ships sailed first to the African coast to capture negroes, who were then shipped to the West Indies to sell to the Spanish.[17]

Trading with the Americas raised a number of special problems for the English merchants. In 1493 Pope Alexander VI divided the New World between Spain and Portugal, giving the Spanish the greater share and exclusive rights over the Church. While the Portuguese had only a small colony on the River Plate, the Spanish rapidly colonized much of central and southern America. Spain's twin interests in evangelizing the Indians and in exploiting their mineral wealth, meant that other Europeans were not tolerated on American soil.[38] The Spanish intended to keep their gold and silver to themselves. However, the Spanish colonists needed slaves and, far away from the stern legislation of their government in Madrid, some governors of Spanish settlements were prepared to turn a blind eye to English slave traders. Under these conditions trading with the Spanish was a chancy business, depending on the laxity of local officials; but it was also very profitable. John Hawkins had already made two successful voyages to the West Indies in the early 1560s, but on this first trip of Drake's, under Captain Lovell, the Spanish treasurer in the little town of Rio de la Hacha refused to buy, even though the slaves had been ordered from Hawkins. Eventually Lovell had to abandon his negro cargo as he could no longer feed them, and the Spanish received ninety slaves for nothing.[17] This voyage was the beginning of Drake's education in deep sea sailing and in the perfidy of the Spanish, as he saw it.

Drake returned home to the news that his father had died at Upchurch. As their mother had died some years previously, there was no reason to keep the Drake sons in Kent and it may be that it was at this time that Francis' younger brothers, John, Joseph and Thomas, came to Devon to join him. The previous year, their grandfather, John Drake of Crowndale, had also died and his widow Margery later sold the lease of the farm. She may have moved from Tavistock to Plymouth, to share a home with her grandsons, until her death in 1571, although other branches of the Drake family continued to live in Whitchurch and Tavistock.[1, 27]

Hawkins' next expedition was supported by Elizabeth I who contributed two old ships, and by Admiral Wynter of the Navy Board. The queen permitted Hawkins to fly the royal standard; in return for her investment and her authorization, she expected a profit. Like her seamen, Elizabeth wanted a share in the fabulous wealth of the Americas, providing it could be achieved without too much political embarassment. The six ships left Plymouth in October 1567, with Hawkins in the queen's *Jesus of Lubeck*. Drake sailed with him, first as an officer in the *Jesus* but soon as captain of the *Judith*, a small barque of fifty tons. It was Drake's first independent command in the Hawkins fleet. Obviously Lovell's failure had not affected Drake's standing in Hawkins' eyes. After a stormy crossing of the Bay of Biscay the English reached the Guinea coast and captured several hundred negroes with the help of an African chieftain. Hawkins led the fleet on the slow middle passage to the West Indies, where they traded for a couple of months without much trouble. Even the governor of Rio de la Hacha was forced to agree to trade, although here Hawkins attacked the town to persuade the Spanish to buy his slaves.

On the way home to England, off the Florida coast, the little fleet was struck by a hurricane and driven westwards again to the small Spanish port of San Juan de Ulloa. This was the port of Vera Cruz, where the main Plate Fleet assembled to carry the silver to Europe. Hawkins was given permission to revictual and repair his ships and when the Plate Fleet arrived the agreement was ratified and hostages exchanged. However, the newly appointed Viceroy of Mexico, Don Martin Enriquez, sailing with the Spanish fleet, saw the Englishmen as dangerous intruders into a purely Spanish sphere and did not feel compelled to abide by their agreement. The Spanish therefore unexpectedly attacked the English ships: the *Angel* was sunk, the *Swallow* and the *Jesus* so badly damaged that they had to be destroyed and many men were killed or captured. Drake stood off in the *Judith* and managed to make his way home, while Hawkins limped after him in the *Minion*. In all, Hawkins lost over three hundred men to the Inquisition, the sea or hostile shores.[17]

*An early English ship*

This incident confirmed Drake's hostility towards the Spanish. To begin with, they were Catholic and to add to the Drake family's experiences of Catholicism at Tavistock, there were the Marian persecutions chronicled by his friend John Foxe in *Foxe's Book of Martyrs*, as well as the anti-papist views of Edmund Drake. On ideological grounds alone Francis Drake found Spain inimical. His personal experience of the Spanish, at Rio de la Hacha and San Juan de Ulloa, sharpened this enmity.

The events at San Juan showed clearly that trading with the New World could no longer continue safely, even on the old ad hoc lines. Since peaceful trading was now impossible, men like Drake turned to plundering instead. This was more profitable though more dangerous; baiting the Spaniards became something of a national sport. What against other nations might have been regarded as piracy was licensed against the Spanish as privateering with the tacit support of the queen herself.[22]

# 7

# The Privateer

The political tension between England and Spain heightened over the next decade, exacerbated in part by the activities of the English privateers on the Spanish Main. Under the devious, intelligent Elizabeth, England became the acknowledged leader of the Protestant powers of Europe, opposed by the rigid orthodox Catholicism and formidable power of Spain. In England Philip of Spain supported the Catholic heir to the English throne, Mary Queen of Scots, through several tortuous plots against Elizabeth. The imprisoned Mary Queen of Scots was a focus for Catholic hopes in England, especially since the papal bull excommunicating Elizabeth in 1570 freed Catholics from their duties as subjects and encouraged conspiracies to murder her. The covert activities of Ridolfi, Throckmorton and Babington against Elizabeth were secretly supported by the Spanish ambassador in London while for her part Elizabeth sanctioned the raids English privateers made on distant Spanish America, as well as supporting the Dutch rebels against Spain in the Netherlands. Despite these unfriendly activities on both sides, official relations between Elizabeth and Philip were amicable if sometimes strained.[39]

From the English point of view open war with Spain, the colossus of Europe, was something to be avoided for as long as possible. As a result of earlier Hapsburg dynastic alliances, made to secure extra territories, on his accession to the throne in 1555 Philip had inherited lands in Italy, the Low Countries and the Mediterranean as well as Spain itself and all her New World conquests.[38] Then, as Mary Tudor's husband, he had also been King of England but when Mary died, Elizabeth refused his offers of marriage. Against the accumulated resources of the Spanish empire Elizabeth had only one small island and a relatively impoverished royal purse. As a shareholder in many privateering voyages, the queen received her share of the profits. To that extent it was in her interests to encourage men like Drake: they could always be disowned if it

King Philip II of Spain, the Low Countries and the Americas

became politically expedient. It was against this shifting background of national rivalry that Drake became the most successful privateer of all Elizabethan sea captains.

Shortly after Drake's return to England in 1569, he married Mary Newman, from the parish of St Budeaux on the Tamar estuary north of Plymouth.[15] Although their marriage lasted fourteen years, Drake was never at home for long and in 1570 and 1571 he made two voyages of reconnaissance to Spanish America. His intention was to capture some of the Spaniards' treasure: his motives were mixed, partly revenge for the treachery he had experienced earlier (although he rarely killed), partly an ambitious drive for wealth, and partly the sheer excitement and challenge of it all.

Typically Drake planned his raids with great care. Wherever possible he surveyed the port and its approaches well before launching an attack. It was clear that for a prolonged expedition he would need a secure base for his operations near the Spanish treasure routes. In 1570 and 1571 he explored the American coast of the Panama Isthmus, where the silver from the Potosi mines of Peru was carried overland by mule trains from the Pacific to the Caribbean coast. The treasure was stored at the town of Nombre de Dios and it was here that Drake judged the Spanish to be most vulnerable. Further east, along the Darien coast, he found a sheltered inlet ideal as a hidden base, which he named Port Pheasant. With his preparatory work done, Drake sailed again in 1572 to make his fortune.

The two small ships of Drake's force, the *Swan* and the *Pasco*, were crewed largely by his friends and neighbours from Plymouth and the small towns of the hinterland. Possibly there were some old friends or relatives from Tavistock on board: one of the quartermasters, Charles Glubb, who was later killed in action, probably came from the Tavistock family of that name; while two of Drake's brothers, John and Joseph, also sailed with him to Port Pheasant. The attack on Nombre de Dios was planned carefully. The raiding party sailed along the coast in three small pinnaces, brought from England in pieces and reassembled by Drake's carpenters. They entered the town at night in two bands, to give the impression of an armed host - in fact Drake had only seventy-three men. After a brief but sharp exchange of fire, leaving casualties on both sides, the Spanish defenders retreated leaving Drake to lead his men in search of treasure. They found the Governor's house, where there were tons of silver left unguarded, but Drake spurned this lesser metal. He wanted gold and precious stones, which he expected to find in the king's Treasure House. His men broke into the Treasury, and found it empty. At this critical moment, Drake collapsed from loss of blood; unknown to his men he had earlier been wounded in the leg, and eventually he had to be carried back to the pinnaces. Without his leadership the silver was abandoned and the enterprise profitless, except for a shipload of Canary wine captured on the way out of harbour.[22]

Fortunately Drake soon recovered and in retrospect the English were persuaded that the storming of Nombre de Dios was a success rather than a disaster. After all, there was still plenty of treasure. In the next few months

Drake took his men up and down the coast disrupting Spanish shipping and then, with the help of Cimaroons, escaped slaves living in the jungle, the English made a successful ambush on the mule trains from Panama. There was more gold and silver that they could carry back to the pinnaces, so most of the silver was buried, and the next day they came back and dug it up. With this their voyage was made.

By this time Drake's small force was seriously depleted. Some men, including his brother John, had been killed in the fighting, while others died of yellow fever; among them Drake's other brother Joseph. There were not enough men to crew both ships so Drake sank the *Swan*. This left him with the leaking *Pasco* and rather than risk the Atlantic crossing in her, Drake captured a Spanish frigate and sailed home in that. With a final touch of insolence he hoisted the St George's flag as they passed close to the harbour at Carthagena, and made a good crossing home in just over three weeks, leaving the Spanish in impotent rage.

After fifteen months at sea, Drake returned to Plymouth in August 1573, in time to interrupt Sunday services. He brought with him great treasure, enough to make him one of the richest men in the West Country. He also brought back the inspiration for a new, yet more daring enterprise - to sail into the Pacific. During one of his forays into the jungle with his Cimaroon allies, from a high tree on the mountain ridge of the Isthmus, Drake had been given his first sight of the Pacific Ocean, or the 'South Atlanticke' as he called it. Immediately it fired his imagination with the desire to be the first Englishman to sail there, and it was towards this end that Drake now began to plan.[3]

# 8
# The World Encompassed

**D**rake came back to be acclaimed a hero in Plymouth, but he soon discovered that politically his success was ill timed. After the Ridolfi plot against the life of the queen two years before, encouraged by the Spanish, both Elizabeth and Philip were eager to improve their relations. Trade with Spain was resumed and Elizabeth closed her harbours to the Dutch sea beggars who were fighting their Spanish overlords. Fundamentally the differences between the two sides were as great as ever but in this new atmosphere it was not the time to acknowledge Drake as the despoiler of Spanish territories. It was certainly not the time to apply to the queen for permission to sail the Spanish dominated Pacific, so Drake judged it expedient to drop out of sight for a while. He probably spent the next two years supporting the government's efforts to subdue Ireland, where foreign Catholic mercenaries, Scots, English Protestants and the divided Irish were bogged down in interminable warfare.

From this period Drake made an important new friend, Thomas Doughty, who became secretary to the queen's rising favourite Christopher Hatton. This friendship with Doughty gave Drake an entry at court which he was able to use to further his plans. By this time Drake was not just one of Hawkins' sea captains - he was well known in his own right. Now a burly thickset man in his thirties, he had three ships of his own, and property in Plymouth, while his reputation as an exceptionally skilful master mariner was recognised at court. As well as his friendship with Doughty, Drake had other useful connections. His cousin, John Hawkins, became Treasurer of the Navy in 1577, while his namesake Francis Russell, known since Tavistock days, was now Earl of Bedford.[36] But despite his West Country fame and his riches, Drake was a provincial of low birth and social standing and his forthright manner and enthusiastic Protestantism must have singled him out at court.

His saving graces were his undoubted abilities and his confidence in himself, which led Elizabeth's minister Walsingham to support him in this proposed new venture, of sailing into the southern seas in search of the unknown Terra Australis, new trading lands, and treasure. Walsingham believed that war with Spain was inevitable, so he was not much concerned with the prospect of annoying the Spanish, but Elizabeth's chief minister, the cautious Burghley, still looked to maintain the peace. Burghley would not have approved of Drake's wilder ventures, so he was never told the whole. Drake was never a gentleman, and his command offended some who were, especially Sir Richard Grenville of Buckland Abbey near Tavistock. Grenville had some experience of exploration himself; he too had proposed to the queen that he should sail for Terra Australis. As an aristocrat Grenville might reasonably have expected to be given the command of this new expedition. Not that Drake lacked the proper complement of gentlemen on his ships - led by Thomas Doughty, the ten gentlemen adventurers of England expected to wield their authority over the subordinate mariners. This clash of wills, over who should command, was to provide Drake with almost as much trouble as the Spanish.

The official orders were to sail south through the Straits of Magellan to discover the unknown continent that was believed to lie beyond. In itself this would be a great endeavour, for since Magellan himself had sailed round the tip of South America, and that in 1520, almost all other attempts on the Straits had failed. Once in the Pacific, Drake was commanded to open trade with friendly nations and was expected to return the same way. In practice, to let an opportunist fire-eater like Drake loose in the Pacific amongst unsuspecting Spanish shipping was likely to have further consequences than trade. Probably Elizabeth and Walsingham expected Drake to ravage the Spanish treasure lanes: it was a way of damaging Spain at a distance, making war a less likely sequel; it may be that Drake's secret orders were to act the privateer. Even official orders, about exploration well to the south of Spanish America, were judged too inflammatory to be widely publicised. The officers were informed, but the crew told only that they were to sail to the Levant.[19]

With shareholders such as the Earl of Leicester, Walsingham and Sir Christopher Hatton behind him, Drake was able to fit out five ships for the voyage. His flagship was the *Pelican*, about a hundred feet long and a hundred tons, so full of guns and ammunition and basic foodstuffs that there was hardly room for trading goods. The same was true of his lesser ships, the *Elizabeth*, the *Marigold*, the *Swan* and the *Benedict*, while more room was taken up by four pinnaces, loaded in their component parts against the day they were needed for their shallow draught. In all there were a hundred and sixty four men and boys, mostly Devon seamen but with a sprinkling of the better connected, such as John Winter, son of the clerk of the queen's ships, who was captain of the *Elizabeth*, and John Thomas, one of Hatton's men, captain of the *Marigold*. Drake also took his brother Thomas and his nephew John, who helped record the voyage by painting accurate representations of the coastlines they passed. This was done to provide directions for those who might follow them, for it was a journey into the unknown, without charts to guide them.[18]

*Drake's circumnavigation*

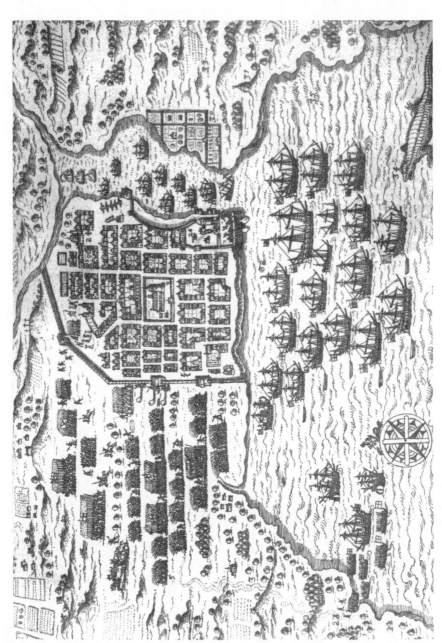

*The Cape Verde Islands, the Port of Santiago*

The fleet left Plymouth in December 1577 and sailed down the coast to Africa. At first they could have been heading for their published destination, the Levant, but the men who had sailed with Drake before were probably not surprised when they left Gibraltar behind them: it seemed as if they were now heading for the Caribbean. It was even possible, though extremely unlikely, that they were heading for the Spice Islands in the East Indies, a Portuguese preserve, as the little fleet was still on the trade route that led around South Africa. An early prize for Drake, captured off the Cape Verde Islands, was a Portuguese cargo ship bound for Brazil: she was valuable to the English chiefly for her captain, Nuno da Silva, a navigator who had detailed knowledge of the coast of South America. In the event da Silva was kept aboard with Drake for fifteen months, treated honourably but later left with a Spanish ship off Mexico. Da Silva was used to the lengthy Atlantic crossing to Brazil; but when Drake told his crew where they were really going, and headed his fleet out into the Atlantic, the Englishmen became unsettled in unfamilar waters.

Once over the Equator, the stars themselves had shifted and the winds were fickle, becalming them on the brassy waters. There were flying fish and strange huge birds and a tropical sun that burnt off the crew's lice. For sixty-three days they saw no land. They had little fresh water and were cooped up together en route to the most dangerous sea passage ever attempted. In these stressful conditions it was not surprising that Thomas Doughty and Francis Drake should quarrel. Although Drake had been put in overall charge of the fleet, a divided command was more usual and as the military commander and social superior Doughty believed that he was more fitted than Drake to be Captain General. There were suggestions that Doughty could use witchcraft against Drake and accusations of pilfering from captured cargoes. Drake believed that Doughty intended to incite a mutiny and decided to deal with the trouble maker before he attempted the passage through the Straits of Magellan, when a united crew would be essential. The real issue was who should command the fleet and when they made landfall, south of the River Plate, Drake brought Doughty to trial.

From the coast of Patagonia there was no question of appealing to the properly appointed authorities in England. As Captain General, with authority from the queen, Drake made himself judge and empanelled forty of the most senior crew to act as jury. Doughty was charged with a number of offences, mainly that he had sought from the beginning to undermine the voyage in speech and with witchcraft, and that he had betrayed the secret of their true destination to Burghley, Elizabeth's chief minister, who did not favour rash adventures against Spain. The jury found him guilty: as judge, Drake sentenced him to death. Before the execution Drake took communion with his erstwhile friend: after it, he began to pull together his divided crew.

There had been some talk from Doughty that gentlemen should not be expected to labour as the mariners did, but Drake would have none of this. He declared that the mariners and the gentlemen should haul and draw together and that any who were not prepared to abide by his conditions could have the *Marigold* to sail home in. No one volunteered to go home. Then Drake took the

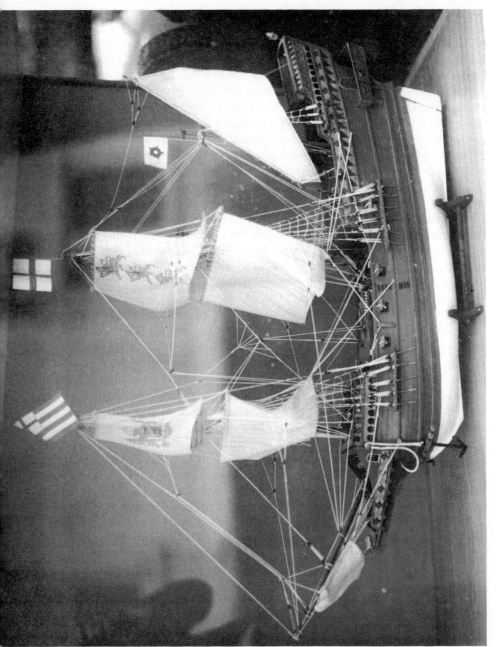

*Model of the Golden Hind, on display at Tavistock Museum*

surprise step of dismissing all his officers but after a brief explanation of the importance of their voyage he reinstated them all again, making it clear that on this venture he was the ultimate authority. A fresh start was made. The *Pelican* was renamed the *Golden Hind* after the arms of Drake's patron Hatton and the fleet, careened and restocked, was reduced to three ships for the attempt on the Straits of Magellan. In August 1578 the *Golden Hind*, the *Elizabeth* and the *Marigold* entered the narrow waters.

It took Drake sixteen days to lead his ships through into the Pacific. To the south were the volcanoes of Tierra del Fuego, to the north the snow-covered mountains of Patagonia, where the inhabitants, aboriginal Indians, were known to be hostile. During the passage the English killed thousands of penguins, enough for seven weeks' supply of fresh meat, and took on fresh water and wood from one of the islands. Navigating this stretch of water took great skill; there were sudden violent squalls, when the wind funnelled between the high mountains, concealed rocks and always the danger of fog. Altogether it was a forbidding experience for the crews of the little English ships. Ironically it was when they reached the open sea again, the Pacific, that the winter gales of the southern hemisphere almost wrecked the venture. The winds were so strong that the ships could only run southwards towards the supposed continent of Terra Australis. The *Marigold* foundered at night and all hands were lost: the *Elizabeth* found the Straits again and fled for home, while the *Golden Hind* was driven so far south as to show that there was not an unknown continent beyond the Straits of Magellan, but that the Atlantic and the Pacific oceans met there.

From this point so far south the *Golden Hind* struggled north again to the South American mainland, where a landing party was ambushed by Indians. Drake and most of the men with him were wounded by arrows and forced to retreat to the ship. There was no surgeon to help the injured, but fortunately most of their wounds were slight. Drake was scarred beneath one eye; two men died; and the rest recovered in time. Another attempt to make contact with the natives was more successful and Drake was shown the way to the Spanish port of Valparaiso, near the gold mines of Valdiva.

They were now in Spanish territory; there was no Terra Australis beyond the Straits and the natives they had met so far had been generally hostile, so trading was impossible. Drake's official orders were no longer valid; but he was loose in the Pacific with an armed ship close to the treasure routes up the Peruvian coast to the Isthmus at Panama and the Spanish did not yet know he was there. It was a situation tailor made for the privateer, who could best serve his country's interests and his own by carrying off Spanish treasure. The opportunistic Drake took his chance and made his fortune. The Spanish ships in the Pacific, masters of all they surveyed, were scarcely armed at all and Drake, with eighteen guns at his disposal on the *Golden Hind*, rarely had to do more than threaten.

This total unpreparedness of the Spanish was not surprising. The only seamen ever to succeed in sailing through the Straits of Magellan had been Spanish and no other Europeans had been seen in the East Pacific. The

Spanish settlements along the west coast were scattered; communications were by coastal shipping as there were no major roads. The news that the English pirate was loose in the Pacific travelled slowly north by merchantmen and small cargo boats. As the alarm filtered gradually northwards so Drake in the *Golden Hind* outran the warnings and was able to plunder still unsuspecting ships and ports. Once the *Golden Hind* was out of sight, no one knew where she was or where she would strike next. Spanish troops were mobilised up and down the coast preparing for Drake's possible return, which interfered with the smooth administration of Peru and Mexico. The mere presence of an English warship proved a disrupting factor to New Spanish government.

The other factor in Drake's success was his good relationship with the American Indians, who were prepared to pilot him or guide him in his attacks on their Spanish masters. This friendliness was due largely to Drake's honesty and good intentions as far as the Indians were concerned. For the Spaniards, the alliance between the English and the Indians had dire consequences - the tally of English successes was impressive.

First Drake took a Spanish merchantman, the *Grand Captain*, at anchor in Valparaiso harbour, and then took the small port itself; from these captures the English came away with gold and church vestments which were given to Fletcher their chaplain. On their way north to the silver mines of Potosi, Drake took the *Grand Captain* with him. It was well known to the Spanish along the coast so it served as a decoy and was also useful as a source of fittings for the *Golden Hind*. In preparation for the stronger defences which lay ahead, Drake broke out and mounted his heavy ordnance and was ready for anything the Spanish could offer. At Tarapaca they captured a llama train carrrying silver: at Arica there was more silver from boats at anchor; after Callao they captured a Panama merchantman which had information about an extremely rich treasure ship, the *Cacafuego*, making its stately way a few hours ahead. Drake gave chase and found the *Cacafuego* had not manned her guns. The captain was unsuspecting and a brief salvo from the *Golden Hind* sufficed to disable her. The prize crew put on board by Drake found treasure in breathtaking quantity. There were jewels and gold and pearls beyond price, and twenty-six tons of silver. The cargo of this one prize was sufficient to make the whole crew rich beyond their dreams and to confirm yet again the wisdom of giving this command to Drake.

Characteristically Drake set the crew of the *Cacafuego* free once their cargo had been transferred to the *Golden Hind*, which was now ballasted by silver. Drake went on north to Coronado Bay where he captured a cargo of Chinese silk and porcelain. With this ship were two China pilots, with their Pacific charts, so Drake took them as equally valuable merchandise. While the *Golden Hind* was being careened again in a secluded bay Drake pondered the alternatives now open to him.

There was no need to look for more treasure, as the *Golden Hind* already held almost as much as she could carry and as much as they could wish for. Behind him, to the south, the hunt was up and the Spanish, expecting him to return by way of the Straits of Magellan, were alerted. To the north there was supposed to lie the fabled North West Passage across North America into the Atlantic and for the master mariner this might be the quickest way home. Hoping to find this new route, Drake sailed on north, briefly capturing the Mexican port of Guatulco on the way, before moving on out of Spanish waters and into unknown territory. Drake took the *Golden Hind* as far north as Vancouver Island before the weather closed in on them. John Dee, the royal astronomer, had predicted the existence of the North West Passage, but Drake found that the coast veered to the north west and not to the east as he had expected. He decided that either the Passage must be farther north, or that it did not exist at all. After such a voyage and loaded with his profits Drake was not prepared to risk everything in further exploration. He turned south again and landed on the Californian coast, where the *Golden Hind* could be refitted and revictualled and the men rested for the next stage of their journey. They were not home yet.[19]

Drake decided to take the one other route open to him, the long trip across the Pacific to the Spice Islands and home again by the way of the Cape of Good Hope. It would be another new experience to sail across the Pacific and it would be an even greater achievement to be the first Englishman to circumnavigate the world. To help him navigate Drake had the two China pilots and their charts on board: but it may be that he would have sailed the Pacific anyway, trusting in his own abilities.

The risks of circumnavigating the globe would have been well known to Drake. Only one other such expedition had successfully attempted this feat and that was sixty years before. That fleet had been commanded by Magellan but only eighteen men and one ship survived; Magellan himself was killed in the Philippines, only half way home. From California more than half the world lay ahead, its currents, winds and landfalls unknown to Drake. If he should, in all the vast watery waste, chance to meet another European ship, it would be an enemy. But Drake was confident in himself, his crew and his small ship, and he knew that he could bring the *Golden Hind* home.

The *Golden Hind* left the coast of New Albion, as Drake had named it, in July 1579 and sailed westwards for sixty-eight days before sighting land again. Drake had taken every care in victualling his ship for the long passage, but by the time they had reached the Spice Islands the crew was weak. Drake lost very few men due to diet related illnesses such as scurvy, as he took great pains to provide fresh food and clean water, but after so long at sea he must have stood in urgent need of fresh provisions.[22]

The Moluccas were the source of spice essential to the European diet, so the Portuguese jealously guarded their monopoly, but Drake was able to trade with one independent ruler, the Sultan of Ternate. Because of all the bullion the *Golden Hind* was carrying, Drake was limited in the amount of spices he could take as cargo, but he did manage to squeeze in ten tons of cloves, ginger and pepper. With this in his holds Drake sailed to the nearby Celebes, where the entire ship's company spent a lazy month on an uninhabited island recuperating from the rigours of their long voyage.

*Drake landing at Nova Albion, America*

By Christmas 1579 they were at sea again and it took them some weeks to sail out of the maze of islands into the Indian Ocean. At one point the *Golden Hind* struck a reef, but fortunately she was not holed; Drake jettisoned half the spices and she floated off into deeper water again on the next tide. For the remainder of the voyage Drake kept out of sight of other ships: with a cargo like his, traversing the Portuguese trade routes, it was well to be circumspect.

Drake retained his native caution to the end of his remarkable expedition. On 26 September 1580, he anchored off Plymouth and before entering harbour checked with some fishermen that Elizabeth was alive and well. His future in England depended on this. Had Elizabeth died, and the Catholic Mary, Queen of Scots succeeded to the throne, Drake would never be safe in England. But in the first certain news he had had for three years Drake learned that her Majesty was in health; and with that he entered Plymouth harbour. He was the first Captain to sail his ship right round the world and he had returned with one of the richest prizes in history. It was an outstanding achievement for the poor boy from Tavistock, a feat of seamanship unmatched in his generation.[19]

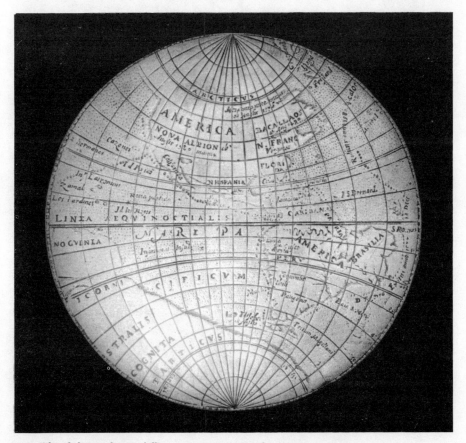

*One side of the Drake Medallion commemorating the circumnavigation*

*Relief showing the knighting of Drake, from the base of the Drake statue, Tavistock*

# 9
# The Hero at Home

**D**rake returned to be acclaimed as a hero throughout England, only to find that the political climate in Europe had altered again. Philip II of Spain was about to take control of Portugal and so unite the two great overseas empires, making himself even more powerful than before. Elizabeth was anxious not to offend him by feting Drake, yet the treasure Drake brought her strengthened her hand against the Spanish. Privately she was grateful to her burly little Devon pirate. The queen's share of the treasure, probably worth about £300 000, was half as much again as her ordinary annual income.[39] With these profits Elizabeth was prepared to ignore the Spanish protests. However, the forms of diplomacy were observed. Edmund Tremayne, a friend of Drake's from Collacombe near Tavistock, was given charge of the treasure so it could be officially registered, but privately Elizabeth ordered him to allow Drake £10 000-worth first. Tremayne worked with Drake on a number of occasions and as an ardent Protestant was delighted to help liberate Spanish treasure. From Trematon Castle it was taken to the Tower to await return to the Spanish, but circumstances prevented its restitution; the queen meanwhile took charge of it. Thus Elizabeth, the other shareholders and Drake were so much the richer, with a return of four thousand seven hundred per cent on their original investment.

Elizabeth summoned Drake to Richmond to describe the journey to her and kept Drake with her for six hours of private speech, as fascinated as anyone by the tales he had to tell. Soon the marvels they had seen, the dangers and difficulties they had overcome, were widely known. On a rising tide of public acclaim Drake brought the *Golden Hind* round to Deptford, where the queen came to visit him. There she asked the French ambassador to knight Drake, in an astute political move which involved the French in this official recognition of the master pirate. Now one of a select band of some three hundred English gentlemen, Sir Francis Drake, royal favourite and national hero, returned in triumph to Devon.[17]

As a member of the gentry Drake had climbed into the higher echelons of society by his own efforts. Self-made men were not uncommon in Tudor England but normally the process of gentrification took several generations. Born a shearman's son, Drake remained a parvenu in the eyes of the established landed classes. Land was still the basis of power under Elizabeth; having been granted the rank, Drake chose to buy the estates to support it. The queen had already made him a landowner by granting him the manor of Sherford in Devon, which Drake leased out to the Maynards, old friends from Tavistock; but when Drake came to make a home for himself he elected to return to familiar country. His choice fell on Buckland Abbey, home of the Grenvilles, less than four miles south of Crowndale where he had been born. As children there had been a great gulf between Drake and Richard Grenville. Drake was an obscure commoner, while Grenville was the son of the captain of Henry VIII's flagship, the *Mary Rose*; when the *Mary Rose* sank off Portsmouth in 1545, Roger Grenville was drowned with the rest of the crew, but the young Richard was left in the care of his wealthy grandfather and was heir to the baronetcy.[29] As men, Drake and Grenville had been rivals for the command of the expedition to Terra Australis and probably Grenville would not have chosen to sell his home to Drake, even though it was on the market. However, Drake was prepared to pay an excellent price, with the bullion he had brought back on the *Golden Hind*, and Grenville's sound business sense defeated any personal antagonisms that may have existed. Two friends of Drake's, Christopher Harris and John Hele, acted for him in the purchase of Buckland Abbey in 1581. The estate was extremely expensive - £3400 - but it provided a fitting background for the new gentleman: it was ostentatious enough to suit his flamboyant character, and the possession of it emphasised that Drake was now on equal terms with the Grenvilles and all their class.[13] It also brought him home.

Buckland Abbey was a thirteenth-century Cistercian foundation acquired by the Grenvilles shortly after the Dissolution of the monasteries, in 1541, and converted into an impressive private house. Richard Grenville had erased the traces of monasticism as far as he was able; the cloisters had been demolished and the great bell sold to Tavistock to be rehung there in 1574, while the abbey church itself had been partitioned into three floors to make living accommodation.[29] From his chambers Drake could look down into the valley of the River Tavy only a few miles downstream from Tavistock, the nearest market town for the Buckland household.

Like the Grenvilles at Buckland Abbey, the Russells of Tavistock represented the new order after the dissolution. Gradually the Russells had assumed the duties to the community previously underaken by Tavistock Abbey; the great fair of St Rumon, the monastic school and the relief of the poor had ended with the abbey, but the Prayer Book Rebellion of 1549 had jolted the Russells into an understanding of the perils of their neglect. In 1551 two new fairs were established by royal letters patent and the profits went to a vestry to be

The Great Hall, Buckland Abbey

The elaborate carvings from the panelled room at Buckland Abbey

*Buckland Abbey today*

The east view of Buckland Priory

used for various charitable purposes. The administration of this fund devolved upon a committee known as the 'Eight Men of Tavistock', and under their careful stewardship and the benevolent patronage of the Russells, Tavistock settled into a new era of prosperity. The 'Eight Men' included one Richard Drake, a wealthy landlord, possibly related to Francis Drake, and they were now responsible for education and relief of the poor in the parish.[27] The vestry fund was used in part to establish a school again in Tavistock, and in 1588 John Drake, probably the uncle of Francis Drake, was appointed Master of the School. The parish church provided many of the services for the town, and here other Drakes were busy; Ellis Drake blew the organ and William Drake kept the clock.[7] Tavistock had its weekly Friday market and its great fairs of St Mark, St Andrew and Michaelmas, to attract the household from Buckland, while Drake had old friends as well as family connections in the town, all doubtless flattered by their association with England's hero.

Eight miles to the south of Buckland Abbey lay Plymouth and the sea, but Drake was kept busy on shore for the early 1580s. As well as his estates at Buckland he had acquired much property in Plymouth where he was now one of the greatest landlords, and he had added a half share in the manor of Sidbery, with John Hawkins.[14] As well as his lands, his mills and the tenements now his to admininster, there were official duties to be discharged. He was elected Mayor of Plymouth in 1581, with a stipend of £20, and Member of Parliament for Bossiney, a constituency on the north Cornish coast, in 1584. Other public duties included those of magistrate and the ordering of local militia for the defence of Devon.[6] This period was also marked for Drake by the death of his wife Mary in 1583. When they married, he was one of the sea captains in John Hawkins' fleet: he had brought her fame and riches, but Mary had spent most of her married life waiting for him to return from the sea. She was buried in the church of St Budeaux, where they had been married fourteen years before, and Drake resumed his busy life. He had his duties in West Devon to perform, while the queen, his greatest patron, expected his frequent attendance at court.

Her Majesty's government also required Drake's participation in another important new sphere. This was the reform of the navy. Since Henry VIII, English sovereigns had neglected the fleet and Elizabeth had inherited a decaying old-fashioned force. For the first part of Elizabeth's reign there was no money to spend on refurbishing the navy and what money there was tended to line the private pockets of the Navy Board. With the appointment of a professional, John Hawkins, as Treasurer of the Navy, there was a new beginning for English maritime power. Hawkins' last voyage had been to San Juan de Ulloa with Drake in 1569 and while Drake's revenge for Spanish treachery was to plunder the New World, Hawkins instead set himself the task of building a fleet that could challenge Spanish supremacy at sea. Hawkins' experiences had shown him that the traditional carrack, clumsy and built to carry men not guns, needed modifying in two major respects. First, English ships needed to be more seaworthy, longer in length in relation to their beam, able to sail the oceans as well as the Channel.[24] The fighting galleon *Revenge*

*Elizabeth Sydenham, the second Lady Drake, niece of John Fitz of Fitzford, Tavistock*

was the first ship to be built according to Hawkins' new designs and she became Drake's favourite; others soon followed. Hawkins' second modification to traditional plans was to increase the number and weight of guns to each ship carried, and to reduce its complement of soldiers. This had profound implications for warfare at sea. Instead of the old practice of grappling and boarding enemy vessels, the new ships were able to disable or even sink the enemy with broadsides from a distance. Although the responsibility for these changes lay with Hawkins, he did not work in isolation. He was advised by other experts including Drake, Frobisher and Raleigh and with their help Hawkins was able to carry through a major building programme and to reform the administration of the navy. By 1587, when Hawkins retired from office, the navy, moribund before, consisted of twenty-three fine fighting ships. The defence of England was at last on a sound footing.[39]

These affairs of state did not prevent Drake from attending to domestic details. Buckland Abbey had come to him without much land, only the original demesne land worked by the monks themselves, so Drake increased his estates. He bought the manors of Yarcombe, in the Blackdown Hills, and Sampford Spiney near Tavistock.[2] Both these acquisitions had their sentimental side, as Yarcombe used to belong to the Drakes of Asshe, the well-born family with whom Drake had once longed to be connected; while Sampford Spiney, a small manor on the edge of Dartmoor, was only three or four miles east of his home town of Tavistock, above the River Walkham which joined the Tavy a couple of miles above Buckland. Buying Sampford Spiney knitted Drake still closer to the countryside he had known as a child.

Wealthy and now a widower Drake was probably the most desirable match in the kingdom, even if he was now in his early forties and inclined to put on weight through his easy life ashore. In 1585 he married Elizabeth Sydenham, a twenty-year-old heiress from Somerset, the daughter of Sir George Sydenham of Combe Sydenham. It was a typical Tudor dynastic alliance. In his second wife Drake found beauty and gentility and this marriage anchored him firmly in the upper classes of England. Like his choice of Buckland Abbey as a home, Drake's choice of bride was significant for the Tavistock connection. Elizabeth Sydenham was related to John Fitz of Fitzford, Tavistock, a family long known to Drake; Elizabeth's aunt, Mary, was married to John Fitz.[20]

Sir Francis and Lady Elizabeth Drake entertained frequently at Buckland during the following years, but Drake was never a man for a settled domestic life ashore. Within six months of his marriage he was at sea again, leading another fleet across the Atlantic.

# 10

# The Approach of War

While Drake was occupied peacefully at home, events in Europe increased Anglo-Spanish antagonism. The Throckmorton Plot of 1583 to assassinate Elizabeth and crown the imprisoned Mary, Queen of Scots, involved the Spanish ambassador Mendoza. The conspiracy was discovered in time and Mendoza was expelled from the country, although Mary, as before, emerged unscathed. The expulsion of the Spanish ambassador exacerbated the tension between England and Spain and matters were made worse when the leader of the Dutch rebels against Spain, William of Orange, was himself assassinated in 1584. It seemed as though Spain would at last crush the rebels and take full control of the Low Countries, which would give her a cross-channel base from which to attack England. Since the excommunication of Elizabeth in 1570, the English had feared a Catholic invasion; now it seemed that the threat was about to materialize.

In terms of money, ships and men the Spanish were much the stronger. Against them Elizabeth had her newly built navy and a small group of men who had grasped that the navy could be England's best offensive weapon. Previous fleets had been used to convey soldiers along the coast and occasionally to provide bases for hand-to-hand fighting. With privateers and adventurers such as Drake in command, the navy could be used to deliver long range attacks, even across the Atlantic. The concept of sea power was slowly being developed.[39]

As part of this change in naval strategy Drake was chosen to lead a new expedition to the West Indies, to damage Spanish shipping and take some of the silver upon which the Spanish economy depended. Relations between England and Spain had deteriorated beyond repair by this time and whereas previously Burghley had discouraged such expeditions, in the hope of averting war, he was now prepared to support this aggression. Officially, however, the two countries were still at peace and Drake feared that the queen might change her mind again

*Portrait of Drake after the circumnavigation of the world*

at the last minute and recall him. In haste, then, the fleet of twenty-nine warships, led by Drake's *Elizabeth Bonaventure*, left Plymouth in the September of 1585 bound for the Caribbean. It was Drake's first time at sea for five years, but he soon showed that his flair for the unexpected had not deserted him. They had left Plymouth in such haste that the fleet was short of water and provisions, a matter which Drake remedied in the most spectacular way available - by landing in the Spanish port of Vigo, where the English took on board supplies and, when the Spanish protested, took the cathedral plate as well.[17] This characteristic Drake touch left the Spanish seething while the English sailed off across the Atlantic to raid the Spanish empire further afield.

The New Year of 1586 found Drake off Santo Domingo where the Spanish were busy preparing for a wedding feast, one of the highlights of that year's social events: instead of the wedding, the Spanish had to face a classic land and sea pincer movement, with the fleet bombarding the town from the seaward side and Carleill's soldiers advancing overland in the Spanish rear. It was an outstandingly successful combined operation and, caught between the two English forces, the Spanish fled into the jungle. The deserted city was abandoned to the English marauders, who put it to the torch, although despite the best efforts of the seamen the more substantial buildings would not burn. The Spanish governor and Drake haggled over the ransom value of the remaining two-thirds of the town and during negotiations Drake's messenger, a negro boy, was casually murdered by one of the Spanish envoys. To European settlers in the Americas the lives of Indians and negroes were of little account, but to Drake this was murder, as well as a personal insult. He demanded that the Spaniard responsible should be executed: nothing was done, so Drake himself executed two of his hostages, Spanish friars, and threatened to kill all of his hostages, two a day, until justice was seen to be done. It was the only time Drake ever killed a prisoner. The next day the Spaniard was executed by his fellow countrymen and negotiations were resumed under a veneer of courtesy. In the end Drake accepted 25 000 ducats for the city and sailed on to Carthagena.

The advantage of surprise was long gone. After a month at Santo Domingo the whole of Spanish America was warned that Drake was again on the rampage. Protected by mangrove swamps and a lagoon, Carthagena's natural defences had been augmented by a strategically placed, heavily armed fort, poisoned stakes on the foreshore and a chain across the entrance to the harbour. Carthagena should have been impregnable. But Drake's reputation went before him to discourage the defenders and in another combined attack, this time at night, Drake and Carleill took the town with the help of the Cimaroons Drake had befriended fifteen years before. Once taken the town was given over to the looters and later ransomed for 110 000 ducats. By this time the English forces were severely weakened by sickness that spread rapidly through the fleet, probably yellow fever. Drake had left England with about two thousand three hundred soldiers - twelve companies - and a thousand seamen, few enough for his cherished project of an attack on Panama; with losses from disease and battle of up to thirty per cent, he did not

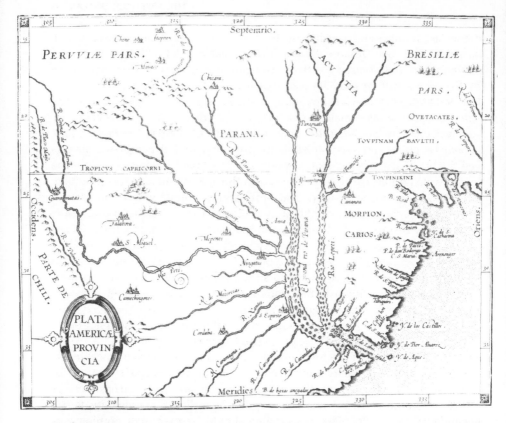

*Carthagena*

*Drake's compass*

have enough men left for this.[17] Leaving Spanish territory in a high state of nervous expectation, Drake sailed instead for Virginia and England's first colony.

Because the first explorers, Portuguese and Spanish, had claimed a monopoly on the rich lands lying along the Equator in central America and the Far East, the English, as late-comers, were forced to concentrate their attentions on the less hospitable regions of the north and south. Drake's voyages, though perhaps the most noteworthy, stand against a background of Elizabethan exploration, north-west to Newfoundland and north-east to Muscovy. The English settlement at Roanoke in Virginia, inspired by Raleigh, was the first of the English attempts to found their own colonies following the Spanish example. Unfortunately the climate and the Indians of the east coast of North America proved inhospitable and when Drake arrived the would be colonists were only too anxious to go home with him. Raleigh had entrusted the colony to Sir Richard Grenville; the colonists were waiting for him, but rather than wait any longer, all of the colonists under their governor Lane took passage home with Drake. So ended the first English settlement in North America. Instead of exploration, the priority for Englishmen now was defence against the Spanish.[37]

Drake returned home again to Plymouth in July 1586. As a punitive expedition the voyage had been a success, but as a joint stock venture in search of profit it was not so fruitful, as the value of the declared plunder did not cover the costs. As usual in Drake's ventures, the sums lost by the Spanish were only a fraction of the wealth Philip was able to extract from his overseas empire, and Spain's ability to wage war was not much damaged: but the same sum represented a disproportionately large increase in England's ability to defend herself.

The question of English defence was now a more pressing matter than ever. The attack on the West Indies was matched by another Catholic backed attempt on the life of Elizabeth in favour of Mary, Queen of Scots, the Babington plot of 1586. Mary was found guilty of this conspiracy and at last, in 1587, Elizabeth brought herself to sign the death warrant of her prisoner queen. Before her death, Mary bequeathed her right to the English throne to Philip, in the hope that the Catholic cause might eventually triumph.[5] With Mary dead, Philip asserted his own right as the husband of Mary Tudor, the last Catholic ruler of England. If he could succeed in invading England, Philip intended to rule as king. But although the death of Mary provided Philip with a righteous pretext for invasion, he was spurred on by events in the Netherlands where his rebellious subjects were supported by the English. From 1585 Elizabeth had maintained an English force in the Netherlands and although its first campaign was a disastrous failure, it soon became clear that the Spanish could not reconquer the Netherlands while there was an English army there. With the English in the Netherlands and Drake in the West Indies, Spanish prestige suffered a severe battering. The answer was to subdue England once and for all.

Preparations for an invasion of England could not be hidden, even if Philip's officers did try to enforce secrecy. There were ships to be built, uniforms to be made, barrels, ordnance, shot and sail to be collected, ships

The Golden Lion

biscuit to be baked, meat and fish to be dried and packed - a thousand essential tasks to be performed. English agents in Europe, from cities as far afield as Strasbourg, Biscay and Antwerp, reported rumours of Spanish plans and in February 1587, Sir Christopher Hatton gave details to the House of Commons. The approaches to England were now defended by the wooden walls of a powerful navy; any Spanish invasion could only succeed if this navy could be evaded or destroyed. Conversely, if the Spanish fleet could be disabled then there could be no invasion. This was the reasoning behind Drake's next voyage.[5]

Philip planned to use his fleet firstly to destroy the English navy, then to help convey the invading army from the Netherlands, where the Spanish general the Duke of Parma was attempting to subdue the Dutch, across the Channel to a point near the Thames. From there, Parma and his men could march straight into London. Obviously for the English the first priority was to sabotage the lengthy Spanish preparations by destroying the assembled ships in the harbour. This was to be an extremely dangerous project, demanding courage and the ability to handle men and ships in the most demanding of all situations - in enemy waters under fire. It was a venture tailor-made for Drake.

The English fleet sailed from Plymouth at the beginning of April 1587 by royal command, narrowly missing a last minute recall by the queen. An attack on the king of Spain's ships in a Spanish harbour amounted to an act of war and characteristically Elizabeth wavered between the need to attack and her desire for peace. Always her captains were impatient to be gone before she could change her mind. On this occasion Elizabeth's messenger took ship after Drake but failed to deliver the new orders; the queen may have deliberately delayed in sending her message, and Drake certainly did not wish to receive it. He was bound for Cadiz with the wind behind him and the Spanish ahead.

Drake's flagship, the *Elizabeth Bonaventure*, headed a fleet of twenty-three ships that arrived in Cadiz Roads on 19 April. The harbour was packed with ships when Drake announced his plans to his fellow captains. He intended to sail straight into Cadiz and destroy all the shipping he could and his orders to them were to do the same. There was an inspired audacity about the plan that carried most of the captains with Drake, but it was the sort of enterprise that in lesser hands would have lead to disaster. Cadiz was full of ships, true, but these were protected by a fortress overlooking the narrow channel into the inner harbour. There were armed galleys within that, powered by oars, and thus not dependent on the wind as the English ships were.[37]

Drake did not give his captains time to brood over these difficulties. Borough, his vice admiral and a cautious man, objected to Drake's plan but was overridden; reluctantly he followed the rest into the outer harbour. The galleys that came out to ram them, relying on superior manoevrability in calm waters, were forced back by broadsides from the heavier English guns and retired to their fortresses. Some French ships fled: one ship gave fight and was sunk; and the remainder, nearly forty, were abandoned to the English. Most of these were pillaged then sunk or burnt. that night the English fleet anchored away from the shore batteries, while the Spanish sent hastily for reinforcements from Jerez. The next morning Borough was anxious to be gone but within the inner harbour lay a galleon belonging to Phillip's admiral Santa Cruz. Drake could not resist such a challenge. He took a flotilla of pinnaces through the narrow channel into the inner harbour and looted and burnt the great galleon, then destroyed all the other ships within reach. Such recklessness alarmed Borough, with the English already under attack from the galleys, fortresses and shore. Drake ordered the retreat: and then the wind died.

The Spanish took fresh heart and brought culverins down to the foreshore to harass the English ships, while the galleys and fireships were prepared to destroy the invaders. In an era of wooden ships soaked with pitch fire was the great enemy, yet the English coolly fended the fireships off rejoicing to see Spanish ships burnt for them. The galleys proved to be no threat at all against the guns of the English fleet. Then the wind blew again and Drake sailed away taking six prizes with him. The English casualties were five men lost and a broken leg for the *Golden Lion's* master gunner, but for the Spanish the whole episode was an unmitigated disaster. In material terms the Spanish lost a great quantity of ships biscuit and wine, intended for the provisioning of the Armada, and upwards of thirty ships, but the real damage was done to Spanish morale. It was said that, in the attack on Cadiz, Drake had singed the king of Spain's beard, it was such a humilating defeat for the pride of Spain. However, beards grow again; and in the aftermath of Cadiz, Drake warned Walsingham to prepare well for the Spanish attack from the sea.[23]

For Drake there was more to do. In all his enterprises, profit as well as politics mattered and so far there had been little enough loot to pay for the voyage. Pausing only long enough to take and destroy the fortress of Sagres, Drake set out into the Atlantic in pursuit of prizes and came up with the Portuguese carrack *San Felipe*, from the East Indies. This was the greatest ship in all Portugal, richly laden with spices, silks, jewels and gold, the most valuable single prize the English had ever taken. Later it was officially valued at £114 000. Once again Drake had humbled the Spanish, enriched himself and his queen and advanced the Protestant cause. When he came into Plymouth in June 1587, Drake brought the news that no Armada could sail that summer and England had won a years' grace. But this success only confirmed Philip in his determination to root out these heretic pirates and their queen once and for all and in Spain the preparations continued.[18]

# 11
# The Defeat of the Armada

The logistical problems facing both sides in preparing their fleets were formidable. Men consumed one to one and a half pounds of ships biscuit a day, whether they were English or Spanish, with salt beef or bacon or fish supplemented by dried beans, this fare being washed down by a gallon of beer for the English and a pint of sherry for the Spanish seamen. Rations could thus be calculated in terms of so many thousand casks of beer or beef, but the corruption endemic in most sixteenth-century navies meant that strict accounting was impossible. Officers demanded larger rations, sergeants claimed to have extra men in service under them, butter went rancid, bacon turned green, ration oil was consumed by the watch lanterns instead of by the crew - administratively it was a nightmare.

Both English and Spanish governments were hard pressed to afford to go to war. The Spanish revenues were much greater that the English, but so were the demands made on Spanish armies. The Duke of Parma, at the head of the invasion force in the Netherlands and awaiting the Armada, was in despair for want of money to pay his troops, while instead of the huge fleet of galleons promised, Philip's reluctant admiral the Duke of Medina Sidonia had only one hundred and thirty sail, of which fewer than fifty were warships. Despite the promises of Pope Sixtus V to give Philip a million gold ducats once England was Catholic once more, and the more immediate help from the safe arrival of that year's Plate Fleet from the Americas, Philip was forced to suspend payments of all kinds in the summer of 1588. In England the naval administration clung thankfully to the pre-Reformation tradition of a Friday fast, to save money on rations, while Elizabeth recruited men as late as possible, and turned them off as soon as the danger was past, all the while seeking to finance the war through the profits of joint stock companies. For Elizabeth, as for Drake, the war was equally a matter of business.

The Spanish admiral, the experienced Santa Cruz, fretted with the difficulties of his command, had died in early February 1588. Philip chose the Duke of Medina Sidonia to succeed him despite Medina Sidonia's ignorance of the arrangements so far and his inexperience of naval warfare. The duke wrote to his king pleading to be released from this duty, but Philip was adamant. The Armada had to be commanded by a great nobleman, and success depended not on the individual but on the will of God. In any event, the Duke of Medina Sidonia was so hedged about by royal orders concerning the Armada that he could do nothing else but comply: no latitude was allowed him in the conduct of the war. His orders were to take the Armada up the Channel to Margate and then to hold the passage for the Duke of Parma to cross with the army. As a convoy, the Armada was expected to fight the English only as a last resort. So the Duke of Medina Sidonia waited through the months of March and April in Lisbon, with the greatest fleet ever assembled under him: like his master the king, he issued detailed instructions to his subordinates regarding such matters as the punishment for blasphemy and the correct watchwords to be used; until at the end of May, Philip commanded the Armada to sail.[5]

The Spring of 1588 was a nervous time of waiting for the English. Short of money as usual, Elizabeth ordered the coastal towns in the West Country to equip ships to meet the Spanish threat; this was to augment the purpose-built warships of her navy and those merchantmen already commandeered. Ships and men came from all over the West Country, from Cornwall, Devon and Dorset, in a patriotic fervour marked by a common desire to take a fair share in the spoils as well as the risks of war. Tavistock, as one of the wealthier boroughs in Devon, was ordered to send three ships of not less than sixty tons burthen, and a pinnace: the same as Plymouth and Exeter, even though it was an inland town. Other ships were ordered from ports such as Saltash, Totnes and Dartmouth. A fair proportion of the ships against the Armada came from Devon, and they were all commanded to join Drake's squadron at Plymouth.[25]

The Lord Admiral of the English fleet was Lord Howard of Effingham, appointed as a capable nobleman of sufficient rank to command the arrogant and dogmatic sea captains, whether gentlemen or yeoman born; but the inspiration for the fleet came from Drake. In Plymouth Sound all the famous names of the age were anchored, Lord Howard in the flagship the *Ark Royal*, Vice Admiral Drake in the *Revenge*, John Hawkins, Rear Admiral, in the *Victory*, with Frobisher in the *Triumph*, while the moorings at Cattewater were choked with sail and the assembled thousands of seamen, packed in tightly, passed rumours and looked to the horizon. The rations intended for sailing were being eaten up, the men were fretful with inactivity, and the longer the crews were mustered the more likely it was that disease rather than the Spanish would kill them. Worst of all for the English sailors, the beer was undrinkable, and this in a fleet where the ration per man was a gallon a day. Drake proposed a bold move -to sail to meet the Armada off Spain, rather than wait for the Armada to come to English waters. There was a real danger here that the English fleet might miss the Spanish altogether, once at sea, and leave England defenceless. However, in the tense weeks of waiting, Drake's

The Revenge

buoyant confidence carried the queen and most of his fellows with him. The queen gave her assent, and the fleet put out to sea at the end of June.[5]

The Armada had spent the month of June in a halting progression up the coast from Lisbon to Corunna. Once at sea the defects of Spanish ship design became painfully apparent. With their high castles and their broad beams even the galleons found it difficult to beat to windward, while for the merchantmen, designed for coastal trade in shallow waters, the task was impossible. Contrary winds delayed the Armada for weeks, time enough to discover another major problem; their food and water was nearly all foul. Supplies had been stockpiled months ahead and by the time the Spanish came to broach the casks there was little fit to eat. Medina Sidonia, at sea with thirty thousand men in poor weather, soon found these problems compounded by mass seasickness, food poisoning and the onset of dysentery. By the end of June the nucleus of the fleet had taken shelter in Corunna harbour, but the majority of the Duke's ships were scattered throughout the ports of the north Spanish coast and as far afield as the Isles of Scilly. The task set for the Armada now seemed impossible to achieve: but the king ordered his fleet to sail on.[21]

Drake had some news of the disaster that had befallen his opponents and it was his fixed intention to repeat his success at Cadiz the year before. The Armada was unprepared, already crippled, lying in harbour waiting for more supplies - another daring surprise attack could finish the threat to England.[16] But for Drake too there were contrary winds and after a slow crossing of the Bay of Biscay the English were forced to put back to Plymouth for fear of missing the Armada altogether. It was then 10 July. Two days later the Armada was reunited under Medina Sidonia and with some fresh provisions, set sail again for England.

The great Spanish fleet made a slow stately progression north, limited to about two knots by the slowest vessels. After a week the Lizard was sighted and on the same day one of the English ships stationed at the mouth of the Channel to watch for the Armada came into Plymouth with the news that the Spanish were within reach. It was the afternoon of 19 July. It was dead low water in Plymouth Sound and the wind was blowing strongly from the south-west, and Drake was playing bowls, to while away the time. It was impossible to take the English fleet out of the harbour against such a tide and wind, so probably Drake did continue his game. There was no possibility of immediate action against the Spanish.

For those concerned with the defence of the realm on land, however, there was plenty to do. A network of beacons had been established to give warning that the Armada was in sight, and from the high point on the Hoe fires could be lit throughout the south. From Plymouth the message would have flickered across the miles to Shaugh Prior, then on to Roborough Down, above Buckland Abbey. The next beacon was at Morwelldown, only a mile or so from Drake's birthplace at Crowndale, to raise the alarm in Tavistock. Then the signal went on to alert other men at other beacons to the north, while from the light on the Hoe the men of East Devon also learnt that the invading fleet was in English waters. If

*Relief showing Drake playing bowls before the Armada, from the base of the Drake statue, Tavistock*

Armada Beacons (Taken from Aspects of Devon History, R. R. Sellman, Devon Books 1985)

all the watchers, stationed lonely on the hilltops, were prompt and if visibility was reasonable, the whole county of Devon could be alerted in half an hour. Once the alarm had been given the muster of fighting men began. Each parish had its pikemen, its arquebusiers and its bowmen.[33] From Tavistock the militia marched down through all the villages to Plympton, led by John Burges beating the drum: as in Tavistock so in towns and villages throughout the county the militia stood to arms.[7] From Plympton the assembled forces could move to counter any attempt at a landing on the south coast of Devon. If the navy failed, the defence of their county, and of England, was in their hands.

That night the English fleet warped out of the Sound, pinnaces and longboats towing the heavy warships against the wind. The next morning, off the Eddystone Rock, the two fleets sighted each other and by the next day the English had managed to beat to the windward of the approaching enemy. From the land the Spanish fleet appeared to be sailing in crescent formation: certainly the ships were sailing very closely together, so that the English could not put in amongst them. The English cannonaded the Spanish for some hours off Plymouth but little damage was caused as the range was too great. In the latest purpose-built warships, such as the *Elizabeth Bonaventure,* up to seventy per cent of the armament consisted of long range guns as part of the shift in naval tactics. The English intended to destroy the Spanish whilst keeping them at arms length, while the Spanish were still trying to grapple and board, and so needed more short range guns. But while the Armada kept its close formation, the English could only bombard those ships on the edge of the fleet.[26] Howard therefore ordered his fleet to follow closely and to attack any Spaniard out of formation. Drake was appointed to lead the first fleet during the night of 21 July but he put out his stern lantern and was found the next morning with the first prize, a disabled Spanish ship the *Rosario.* The instincts of the privateer never died in Drake even during such a national crisis. The *Rosario* was taken into Torbay and the English spent the next day still in the wake of the Armada as it crossed Lyme Bay at a steady two knots.

That day, 22 July, the *San Salvador* began to sink and was towed into Weymouth. Otherwise the Armada was unharmed; nearly half way across the southern coast and still it looked invincible. The next day the wind changed off Portland Bill, giving the Spanish the weather gauge for the first time. This was their opportunity to destroy the English navy and clear the Channel for Parma's invasion force, but even with the wind behind them, the Spanish were unable to catch even one of the nimble English ships and their soldiers were never used. It was the biggest battle so far, with much powder and shot consumed, but the Spanish ships were too ponderous and the English ships still standing too far off for their guns to be effective, to bring the battle to a conclusion. The English had used up so much ammunition that their stores were running low, but they were able to send ashore for more supplies: the Spanish, in much the same position, had no such stocks to draw upon. The next day Howard and Drake planned a concerted attack on the Armada using merchant ships at night, but the wind died before this could be attempted. In desperation the next morning, with both fleets becalmed off the Isle of Wight,

*The Armada sailing up the Channel showing crescent formation. This is an eighteenth-century copy of a sixteenth-century tapestry*

Howard had warships towed into battle by rowboats, but again little real damage was done. It seemed that the two fleets were unable to come to grips effectively.

On shore the course of the Armada had been followed anxiously. There had been some fears that the Spanish would try to sieze the Isle of Wight - it had been mentioned by Philip as a possible secondary objective - but once past the Solent it was clear that Medina Sidonia could not turn back. With the invasion drawing inexorably closer there were fears for the safety of the queen and an army under the Earl of Leicester was stationed to defend her. Elizabeth was the embodiment of England and to lose her would be to lose all.

In the Channel, by 27 July, both fleets were approaching Calais. Medina Sidonia expected to be able to land at Dunkirk but now the pilots explained that this would be impossible - the Armada could not even approach Dunkirk, with its protecting sandbanks, because its draught was too great. Parma had provided only river barges for his army so any crossing in those could take place only in the best of weather. But in the event this was irrelevant, for Parma was as unable to come out from Dunkirk as the Armada was unable to come in; the entrance to Dunkirk was patrolled by Dutch flyboats manned by rebels who would sink Parma's unseaworthy flotilla given the chance. At this point Philip's grand strategy began to collapse under the unfortunate Medina Sidonia. He had faithfully performed his duty, bringing the Armada virtually intact through the Channel despite the best efforts of the English, only to find that the two Spanish forces could not meet. He anchored in Calais Roads that night, debating what course to follow; while downwind the English squadron under Seymour, set to guard the Thames approaches, slipped over the Channel to join up with the main body of the English fleet. Now the English sail outnumbered the Spanish, though to the English this was the most dangerous time, with the Armada within a few miles both of Parma's army and of England.

The Calais Roads made a dangerous anchorage with strong tides and sandbanks on the lee shore, so the Armada took especial care over anchoring. Now the Spanish were vulnerable to the last weapon the English could muster - fireships. Eight merchantmen, of which five came from Drake's squadron, were filled with stores and their guns loaded ready to explode. At midnight the ships were fired: they drifted down on to the waiting Spanish with the wind behind them, blazing with tar and their guns blasting indiscriminately. With his usual attention to detail Medina Sidonia had already warned captains to cut their cables if necessary to avoid any fireships, and then to anchor further out, but with the flaming ships actually bearing down on them most of the Spanish fled out to sea and were scattered. The Armada as a single fighting force had disintegrated; the morning of 29 July found Spanish ships spread out along the miles of coastline with the English moving in for the attack.

The battle off Gravelines lasted all day. Medina Sidonia on the *San Martin* fought a valiant rearguard action against the English ships that came in closer than ever before. For the first time the English guns were able to bombard the Spanish effectively. At close quarters therefore, close enough for the Spanish

PLIMMOUTH

*The Battle off Plymouth*

*The route of the Armada; eighteenth-century illustration*

*Spanish galleon before the wind*

soldiers at last to use muskets, the English sank three galleons and disabled several others. It was a great victory; but in the smoke and confusion no one realised it. During the night the Armada drifted down upon the coast of Zeeland and it seemed the whole enterprise would end in a litter of wrecks; but at the last minute the wind changed and they were saved from the shoals and the Dutch. It was impossible for Medina Sidonia to shepherd his damaged flock back against the wind to Parma, so he and his captains decided their only course was to follow the wind round the north coast of Scotland and make for home that way. The English followed closely into the North Sea, as far as Newcastle, then turned back. There were no friendly ports for the Spanish. Short of water, they threw their horses and mules, brought to pull the land artillery, overboard; short of ammunition they dared not meet enemies. The damage done by the English was nothing beside the damage that storms off Scotland and Ireland were to do.[21,23]

In England prayers were offered for their delivery from the Spanish: in the fleet ships' fever spread rapidly, killing up to five thousand seamen. Problems with victualling the ships continued, partly through sheer parsimony and partly because of continuing bad weather; also the beer continued to be sour. As soon as it was clear that the danger really was past the seamen and soldiers were discharged. Inevitably there was poverty and continuing sickness amongst those who had been turned off. Drake and Hawkins made some charitable efforts to help them when they founded the Chatham Chest for the relief of poor seamen, but it was a perennial problem in the aftermath of the war. Typically Drake himself came out of it well, with the capture of the prize ship the *Rosario* to his credit. To men in Europe the victory against the Armada was credited to Drake, but in England there was a more sober epitaph. The medals the queen issued to commemorate the victory bore the inscription, 'God breathed and they were scattered'.[5]

More than a third of the ships of the Armada, possibly half of them, were wrecked on the coasts of Scotland and Ireland. In all perhaps twenty thousand men died. Some drowned; some starved on inhospitable islands; many died of disease; and some, most cruelly, survived shipwreck only to have their throats cut in Ireland. It was to Medina Sidonia's credit that he managed to bring half of his ships home through foul weather in the Atlantic seas. At the end Philip allowed his faithful duke to retire to San Lucar. It had been a valiant effort but the enterprise had failed; despite all their prayers and exhortations, God had not brought victory in their holy war. This failure of the Armada led to a profound alteration in Spanish self-confidence, as the implications of their defeat spread through Spain and was an important factor in the change from the triumphs of the sixteenth century to the gradual decay of the seventeenth century.[38] But in the Autumn of 1588 it was enough for the English that the queen and Protestantism still ruled; thanks to Drake and the navy, they were safe.

*The Armada portrait of Queen Elizabeth I, attributed to George Gower*

# 12

# Later Years

Despite his glittering successes of the past few years Drake was not content to sit idly ashore and wait for the Spanish to try again. This time he planned to carry the war to the enemy with an ambitious combined land and sea operation against Lisbon. Drake's intention was first to destroy those ships from the Armada that had survived, in harbour on the north Spanish coast; this would remove the danger of another attempt at invasion. Then the fleet would move south to Portugal and restore the exiled King Dom Antonio or, if this was impossible, take the Azores and use the islands as a forward base for attacking the Spanish Plate Fleet on its way across the Atlantic. The military command was in the hands of the experienced Sir John Norris while Drake led the fleet: the venture was financed as a joint stock enterprise with the queen the major shareholder as the Crown alone could not support such expenditure after the bills for 1588 had been met.

Drake's name was enough to bring in the volunteers: visions of glorious deeds and glorious treasure spurred on thousands to sign up under England's most famous adventurer. By the time the huge fleet left Plymouth in April 1589 there were perhaps one hundred and fifty sail, most of them armed merchantmen, with over ten thousand soldiers on board. They sailed with high hopes. Drake was confident, the wind was fair for Spain, while the Spanish were still not recovered from the defeat of the Armada. One of the gentlemen adventurers sailing with Drake was Anthony Ashley, MP for Tavistock in 1588-9[11] and the author of a famous work on seacharts for mariners. Ashley was Clerk of the Privy Council and Burghley had instructed him to sail with Drake: possibly he was there as the government representative, to keep an eye on the queen's investment.[41] Certainly Elizabeth needed the venture to show a profit. She had spent all she could well afford in repelling the Armada, while the cost of fitting out the 1589 expedition had spiralled well beyond the original estimates. Elizabeth had further cause for irritation as her young favourite, the headstrong Earl of Essex, had fled from court and sailed with the fleet, contrary to her orders. All in all, with Elizabeth behind and the Spaniards in front, Drake needed to be successful.

The first task was to destroy what remained of the Armada. Drake made for Corunna, where the troops burnt the lower town but, in an over-ambitious and unnecessary manoeuvre, failed to take the fortified upper town. What shipping there was in the harbour was burnt, although there was only one galleon; certainly this first raid was a success as far as frightening the Spanish went, but unfortunately the English seamen came across a large store of wine. From this time on the expedition became steadily less successful. The large English fleet, manned in part by the blind drunk, was now subject to all the difficulties the Armada had experienced. They were in enemy waters, with insufficient victuals due to the large number of volunteers, carrying soldiers crammed into insanitary conditions. The usual problems of seasickness, overcrowding and disease combined to thin the ranks, so that when the army was landed at Peniche, north of Lisbon, they took days to march the fifty miles to Lisbon. All surprise was lost. The Spanish were waiting for Norris when he finally brought the remnants of his force up to the walls of Lisbon, but there was no pitched battle. Norris could not force the walls as he had no siege guns and in the end he was forced to withdraw to the waiting ships. Drake had earlier been unable to sail up the Tagus due to contrary winds, so the intended land and sea operation had never taken place. With sickness now spreading rapidly through the fleet, Drake decided to make instead for the Azores counting on the chance to intercept the Spanish Plate Fleet and a glorious end to the expedition. But again the wind was against him and so the fleet stopped not at the Azores but at Vigo, where in the last action of the voyage the English took and burnt the town. Then, with the *Revenge* sinking under him and his fleet scattered by storms, Drake came back to Plymouth.[17]

It was not a happy homecoming. Portugal was still Spanish, the ships of the Armada were still being refitted, and the Plate Fleet was safe. Many Englishmen had died, mostly of disease, a few English ships were lost, there was no profit and the queen was angry. The spectacular success expected of Drake had not materialised and the burning of Corunna and Vigo, and the landing of an English army on Spanish soil, were not sufficient compensation. Set to achieve both material gain and strategic advantage, in the end the Portuguese expedition had accomplished neither.

For the next few years Drake settled down comfortably to live the life of a gentlemen ashore. Now in his late forties, an old man by the reckoning of his day, he divided his time between Buckland Abbey and his new house in London, the Herbor, and occupied himself with local issues and the management of his estates. His chief project was the improvement of Plymouth's water supply as the demands of the large fleets could not be met from existing wells and conduits.[6] Water was taken from the River Meavy, below Sheepstor on the edge of Dartmoor, midway between Tavistock and

*'Spry's Plot'. Map of 1584 showing Drake's Leat* (Water from the Moor, D.J.
Hawkings, Devon Books, 1987)

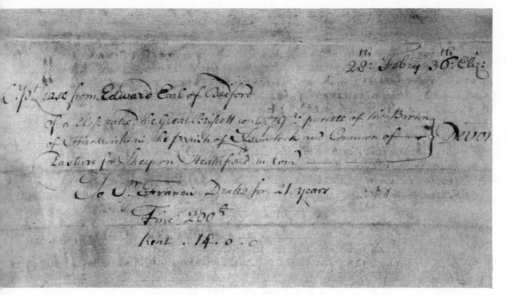

*Lease of pasture at Great Briscott to Drake in 1594*

Plymouth, and brought in a leat some seventeen miles long down into the Millbay. Drake then turned the leat to further good account on his own behalf, by building six profitable corn mills which were driven by the water.[30] Flour from Drake's mills and water from his leat supplied subsequent fleets out of Plymouth.

For a man not born to property Drake managed his holdings shrewdly. As well as building the six new corn mills of his own he also bought the remaining town mills from the Hawkins family, but sold his share in the manor of Sidbury to Richard Hawkins the owner of the other half in 1592.[2] Two years later, in 1594, he leased land at Great Briscott in the parish of, Tavistock from the third Earl of Bedford, Edward Russell, for sheep pasture.[1] Drake had no son to leave these estates to; his heir was his brother Thomas.

From the peaceful daily round in Devon, Drake probably heard of the death of Sir Richard Grenville with mixed feelings. Grenville had preceded Drake at Buckland and he died of wounds received fighting the Spanish from the deck of the *Revenge* in 1591.[29] Throughout their careers the  paths of Grenville and Drake had crossed but now Grenville was dead in a blaze of glory while Drake lived on in Grenville's house. Drake must have wondered if the call to arms would come again or whether he would live out his days in peace. The queen at least had not forgotten him. There were messages from court, and in 1594-5 William Whitchurch of Tavistock went to Buckland on the queen's business.[7] At last, in 1595, Drake was commissioned to go to sea again.

# 13

# The Last Voyage

The great days of the war in the Atlantic were over by the 1590s. The protagonists were getting old now; Elizabeth and Philip were in their sixties, and the generation of Englishmen that had grown to power under the queen was dying. The Earl of Leicester had died in 1588, Walsingham in 1590 and Grenville and Frobisher soon afterwards. Elizabeth's remaining great sea captains were Drake, now in his fifties, and John Hawkins ten years older; despite their age both men were still eager to fight the Spanish once more. The Armada had failed, but there were other armadas, and the silver of the Americas was still the mainstay of Spanish strength. Drake argued that if he could take Panama and block this vital supply line, Spanish troops would mutiny for lack of pay, Spanish ships could no longer be built and Spanish power would collapse. The war would be won.

The logic of this argument appealed to Elizabeth, but there were wider considerations. For the last twenty years France had been paralysed by her Wars of Religion between Catholic and Huguenot but now there was a new French king, Henry of Navarre, the Protestant heir to a Catholic throne, who had ensured his crown by embracing Catholicism. Elizabeth feared that England might be threatened by a resurgent Catholic France as well as Spain, while there were persistent rumours that Spain was ready to invade Ireland. In these circumstances Elizabeth doubted the wisdom of sending a strong force across the Atlantic for fear it might be needed in the Channel to defend England itself. The fleet assembled for the expedition in Plymouth harbour, manned entirely by volunteers drawn by Drake's reputation, and waited while the sponsors argued over its proper objective, until some fresh news sparked off the old lust for treasure in both captains and queen. A Spanish galleon, laden with gold and silver, was reported to be lying disabled in San Juan de Puerto Rico. This news was enough to fire Drake and Hawkins with the desire

*The Defiance, Drake's flagship on his last voyage*

to be off at once for the seas of their youth and it persuaded the queen to give her assent. In August 1595 Drake sailed from Plymouth for the last time; prayers were read in Tavistock after the departure of the fleet.[7] As well as Drake there were several other Tavistock men in the fleet, including Brute Brown and Thomas Maynarde, probably the second son of Drake's tenants at Sherford.[44]

It was a formidable force, with six fighting galleons, twenty-one armed merchantmen, and a thousand soldiers under Sir Thomas Baskerville, commanded by two great admirals. However, there were disagreements between the two commanders. The divided command, intended to produce a balance between the cautious Hawkins and the reckless Drake, led to acrimony instead of results. Meanwhile, the Spanish American empire had learned from the early years of English attacks. Harbours were now properly defended, signals systems set up, merchantmen were armed and the towns guarded. A large scale enterprise such as the English expedition was only likely to succeed with the benefit of surprise, but the English admirals squandered this advantage when they made a leisurely crossing with a detour to Guadeloupe for fresh water. Hawkins especially was reluctant to press home the attack, even on Spanish ships carrying the news of their whereabouts. By the time the English were finally anchored off Puerto Rico, the Spanish had had a week to prepare for them. Altogether it was a bad beginning that rapidly turned worse when it became clear that Hawkins was very ill.[17]

All the problems attendant on any large scale naval expedition - seasickness, ships fever and dysentery - were compounded once a fleet entered tropical waters. An unseasoned crew was subject to yellow fever and malaria, while all the common diseases were accentuated; food poisoning especially became much more of a problem as food decayed quickly in the heat. Sir John Hawkins, aged sixty-three, died on the afternoon that the assault on San Juan began and he was soon followed by many more men in the fleet as disease spread inexorably amongst the crews. It was an ill omen for Drake. He and Hawkins had come a long way since their early voyages together to San Juan de Ulloa: even though Drake had seen many friends and relatives die, the death of this cousin was a reminder of his own mortality as well as a personal loss. During the subsequent attack on San Juan another close friend of Drake's, Brute Brown from Tavistock, was killed by a Spanish cannon ball while at dinner in Drake's flagship, *Defiance*. There was no time for mourning; Drake and Baskerville attempted a combined operation against the Spanish city that night but its defences were too strong. In the end they were forced to withdraw and seek easier prey. It seemed that things had changed in the Caribbean since Drake had last sailed those waters but he was not the man to let one reverse daunt him. Confident still, he led the expedition to Rio de la Hacha, which he knew of old, sacked the town and razed it to the ground. Then he moved on to take Nombre de Dios after Christmas and prepare for the main assault on Panama.

So far the gains had been modest. The Spanish had learnt from earlier losses and now stored their treasure in better defended towns, but there was still

Above: *Relief showing Drake's burial at sea, from the base of the Drake statue, Tavistock.*
Below: *A more romanticized view of Drake's funeral, Burial at Sea by Thomas Davidson*

the major land route across the narrow Isthmus of Panama that remained vulnerable to attack as the Spanish transported the silver from the Pacific coast, where they might reasonably expect to be safe from marauders, to the Atlantic coast for shipment to Spain. If Drake could take Panama he could hold the Spanish empire to ransom. But Panama had three weeks warning and the main pass was fortified against the English. Baskerville and his soldiers made slow progress through torrential rain into the mountains, only to find the pass held stoutly against him. In despair the English retreated to their ships. Panama was safe and Drake's strategy had failed.

Surrounded as they were by Spanish held territory, there was no shortage of lesser targets in Honduras and Nicaragua but the heart had gone out of Drake. After nearly six months at sea many of his men were sick and now Drake himself succumbed to dysentery. He was an old man and the end came rapidly. After three days in his cabin, Sir Francis Drake died at about seven o' clock in the morning of 28 January, 1596. The fleet was at anchor off Puerto Bello and Drake was buried at sea in a lead coffin. It was a fitting grave for the master mariner, the scourge of the Indies.[4]

Without Drake to lead and inspire him, Baskerville brought the fleet home. The news of Drake's death led to national mourning; he had been the great hero of his age. Drake's drum was taken to his home at Buckland and his will read and finally proved. His widow Elizabeth was left a rich woman but in lieu of children of his own, the bulk of his estate was entailed on his brother Thomas Drake.[20] In the seventeenth century Drake's heirs at Buckland maintained the Tavistock connection by becoming Members of Parliament for Tavistock. The family remained major landowners in the area for generations, into the twentieth century, but the memory of the founder of these fortunes. Sir Francis Drake, overshadowed all others.

The death of Drake in 1596 marked the end of an era. Within five years Elizabeth and Philip were also dead and the great war between them dwindled into an exhausted peace. Drake's tempestuous career had inspired the English defence and proved the foundation for English maritime power. During his lifetime the focus of international affairs shifted from the Mediterranean to the Atlantic and Drake's example pointed towards a maritime, imperial future for England.

*Drake's Drum, Buckland Abbey*

# 14
# Drake's Legacy

he news of Drake's death was brought home to Buckland by his brother Thomas, together with his drum, his Bible and his sword. Lady Elizabeth Drake, now about thirty, had ten years of marriage to look back on; glittering occasions at court, the special affection of the people of Devon, triumph and tragedy. Drake's death left her a rich woman with property in Plymouth, but without children and subject to her brother and sister in law at Buckland Abbey. The next year, 1597, she married Sir William Courtenay, a widower with children, and left Buckland Abbey to the Drakes.[17]

Drake's drum was probably used for the last time during the funeral ceremonies when he was buried at sea. It is possible that this was the drum that Drake took on all his later voyages and it remains at Buckland Abbey. The room that Drake ordered to be panelled according to Elizabethan tastes was also preserved by later Drakes, as well as other memorabilia. The abbey itself was entailed on Thomas Drake, who was married to Elizabeth Elford, a widow from Sheepstor: their son Francis Drake was created a baronet and they founded the dynasty of the Drakes of Buckland.[20] After his brother's death Thomas Drake never went to sea again. He was preoccupied with the management of his estates, and with the litigation that arose from challenges to his inheritance.

Drake made two wills, the second in January 1596, the day before he died. By the first will all his manors were bequeathed to Thomas Drake but by the second will the manor of Yarcombe was bequeathed to a cousin, Francis Drake of Esher, providing this Francis Drake paid Thomas Drake £2000, and the manor of Sampford Spiney was to go to Jonas Bodenham, a nephew of Drake's first wife Mary Newman. Thomas Drake challenged these bequests in the Chancery Court, but when Francis Drake of Esher produced the £2000 the Court ordered that he should have Yarcombe.[17]

The dispute over Sampford Spiney was much more acrimonious. Jonas Bodenham had sailed with Drake many times and had the further claim of his relationship to Mary Newman: but Thomas Drake alleged that Jonas Bodenham had embezzled money from Drake, while Jonas Bodenham accused Thomas of rifling Drake's belongings even before his death. In the end the manor of Sampford Spiney was sold back to Thomas Drake for the sum of £300, considerably less than the £500 Sir Francis Drake had valued it at in 1581: possibly there was some truth in Thomas Drake's allegations.[2]

One of the most enduring aspects of Drake's legacy was the provision of fresh water to Plymouth by Drake's Leat. Legends grew up about Drake's part in building the leat; it was said that he rode up on to Dartmoor and the waters of the Meavy obediently followed him down to Plymouth. Indeed, such was Drake's hold on the public imagination that legends attached themselves to many aspects of his life, most notably to his drum, which was supposed to beat whenever danger threatened England.

In Crowndale, Drake's birthplace, the farmhouse owned by his grandparents John and Margery Drake was burnt in 1549 by the Catholic rebels against the New English Prayer Book. Possibly the Drakes were known to be sympathetic to the Protestant cause. Since the building would have been of stone, probably there was little damage that could not be repaired. This Crowndale farmhouse survived until about 1850, although it may well have been altered during the centuries; it was then pulled down and another building erected on the site. In 1926 a plaque was placed on this farmhouse to commemorate the fact that Drake was born nearby in the valley. No cottages from Drake's time have survived in Crowndale, although there are foundations of old houses still visible on both sides of the river.

In Tavistock itself much of the town centre that Drake knew was swept away by the seventh Duke of Bedford when he rebuilt the town in the mid-nineteenth century. But in other respects Tavistock has changed little; the development of the town has been limited by the steep sides of the narrow river valley, and today Tavistock on the north bank of the Tavy is little larger than the borough marked out by the monks in the twelfth century. When the Duke of Bedford, heir to the first Lord Russell of Drake's day, drove the new Plymouth Road over the site of the abbey church to the gates of the old Fitzford House, he provided a suitable site for Tavistock's chief memorial to Drake - the bronze statue, unveiled in 1883, of Drake of Tavistock.

*Medallion struck to commemorate the unveiling of Drake's statue, 1883*

# References

Documents and Documentary Collections
1   Devon Record Office.
    Leases, deeds, etc. from the Bedford Collection.
2   West Devon Record Office.
    Leases, deeds, etc.
3   Sir Francis Drake, Bart. *Sir Francis Drake Revived* (1626)
4   Thomas Maynarde, *Sir Francis Drake His Voyage* Reprinted by the Hakluyt Society.
5   Stephen Usherwood (Ed.) *The Great Enterprise: The History of the  Spanish Armada: Contemporary Documents.*
6.  Plymouth Municipal Records (Worth Collection 1893)
7   Tavistock Parish Records (Worth Collection 1887)
8   Lt. Col. J.L. Vivian, *The Visitations of the County of Devon: the Heralds' Visitations of 1531, 1564 and 1620.* (1895)

Transactions of the Devonshire Association
9   H.H. Drake, *Drake: The Arms of his Surname and Family* Vol. 15
10  Mrs. G.H. Radford, *Edmond and Richard Tremayne* Vol. 33
11  J.J. Alexander, *Tavistock as a Parliamentary Borough.* Vol. 42
12  J.J. Alexander, *Crowndale.* Vol. 46
13  Joyce Youings, *Drake, Grenville and Buckland Abbey.* Vol. 112
14  J. Barber, *Sir Francis Drake's Investment in Plymouth Property.* Vol. 113

Biographies
15  Ernle Bradford, *Drake* (1965)
16  Julian S. Corbett, *Drake and the Tudor Navy* (1899)
17  G.M. Thompson, *Sir Francis Drake* (1972)
18  Neville Williams, *Francis Drake* (1973)
19  Alexander McKee, *The Queen's Corsair* (1978)
20  Lady Eliott Drake, *The Family and Heirs of Sir Francis Drake* (1911)

Maritime

21  David Howarth, *The Voyage of the Armada.* (1981)
22  David Howarth, *Sovereign of the Seas.* (1974)
23  Garrett Mattingley, *The Defeat of the Spanish Armada* (1959)
24  Colin Munro, *Sailing Ships* (1973)
25  M.M. Oppenheim, *The Maritime History of Devon* (1968)
26  D.W. Waters, *The Elizabethan Navy and the Armada of Spain.* (National Maritime Monograph 1975)

Devon

27  H.P.R. Finberg, *Tavistock Abbey* (1951)
28  H.P.R. Finberg, *Westcountry Historical Studies.* (1969)
29  Crispin Gill, *Buckland Abbey.* (1951)
30  Crispin Gill, *Plymouth: A New History* (1966)
31  Helen Harris, *The Industrial Archaeology of Dartmoor* (1968)
32  W.G. Hoskins, *Devon.* (1954)
33  R.R. Sellman, *Aspects of Devon History.* (1962)
34  G. Woodcock, *Tavistock School: the First Thousand Years.* (1978)
35  G. Woodstock, *Tavistock's Yesterdays.* Vol. 1 (1985)

General

36  Georgina Blakiston, *Woburn and the Russells.*
37  William Camden, *The History of the most Renowned and Victorious Princess Elizabeth, late Queen of England*
38  J.H. Elliott, *Imperial Spain.* (1963)
39  G.R. Elton, *England under the Tudors.* (1955)
40  Michael Lewis, *The Hawkins Dynasty: Three Generations of a Tudor Family.*
41  *Dictionary of National Biography.*